Conditioning
for
Rugby League

Conditioning

for

Rugby League

JOHN KEAR

ANDREW CLARKE

and

SIMON WORSNOP

Queen Anne Press

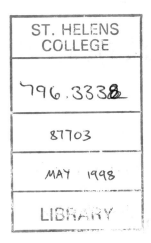
A QUEEN ANNE PRESS BOOK

© The Rugby Football League, 1996

First published in 1996 by
Queen Anne Press
a division of
Lennard Associates
Mackerye End
Harpenden
Herts AL5 5DR

A catalogue entry is available from the British Library.

ISBN 1 85291 572 2

The cover photograph of Andy Clarke was kindly supplied by John Cross

Cover design: Paul Cooper
Design Consultants: Design 2 Print
Editor: Neil Tunnicliffe
Production Editor: Chris Hawkes
Origination: Leaside Graphics

Printed and bound in Great Britain
by Ebenezer Baylis, Worcester

CONTENTS

FOREWORD

This book comes on the back of a conditioning revolution which has taken place in British Rugby League since the nadir of the late 1970s and early 1980s. In those dark days, it fell to a lecturer at the Carnegie School of Physical Education at Leeds Polytechnic, Rod McKenzie and, more significantly, Phil Larder, the former National Director of Coaching and current head coach of the England and Great Britain teams, to take the game of Rugby League forward from a physiological point of view at a rapid pace.

The Rugby League Coaching Manual by Phil Larder, first published in 1988 with an updated second edition in 1992, is recognised throughout British sport as an excellent guide to coaching this great game. However, as with anything, time passes and more information becomes available. The game itself is constantly changing. With this in mind, it was felt to be both prudent and necessary now to analyse the section on conditioning for Rugby League in the aforesaid manual, look at the new evidence which has been unearthed on our exciting, fast collision sport, and produce a comprehensive text on "Conditioning for Rugby League".

This book highlights the background to the developments in conditioning from a Rugby League perspective. It also details a fascinating project commissioned by the Rugby Football League which underlines the necessity for top-quality conditioning for all aspects of the game but, more particularly, for the collision. More and more coaches are acknowledging this as one of the essential ingredients of a successful Rugby League team: "Control the collision, and you control the game."

Following on from this there is some basic exercise physiology relating to types of muscle, how muscles work and the different energy systems involved in exercise, before progressing to strength training, where a full background explanation of this aspect of conditioning leads on to the essential exercises required for a weights programme. Speed is then discussed before practical strategies to develop this are shown, and then the final two elements in any conditioning programme, endurance and flexibility, are dealt with. Since any gains in physical conditioning will not be fully effective without a correct dietary and fluid intake regime, this is the core of the chapter on nutrition.

When delivering information on physical conditioning, there are always posers which are forwarded from the floor. The most common questions have been compiled, and common-sense answers are given which are based on the information provided in the book.

The penultimate chapter deals with the objective measurements of physical conditioning which are so vital to a structured programme. These provide accurate details of a player's physiological state and allow the coach to structure work to develop the player to the best of his physical ability.

These fitness tests are described in full, and the authors would like to thank John Brewer and Jackie Davies from the Lilleshall Human Performance Centre, who work very closely with the Rugby Football League via the Sports Science Support Programme which is supported by the Sports Council for the testing of élite Rugby League players, for their help and input into this chapter.

Finally, a full year's training programme is given both for adults and for the inexperienced – from a conditioning perspective – youth players. It must be stressed that these programmes are for guidance, and the coach should amend them to suit his own needs and those of his individual players. These examples are merely a substantial starting point.

The book illustrates the necessity for any coach to plan, prepare and organise a physical conditioning programme for those in his charge. But conditioning is only one element of the coach's work. He must also develop skills, technique and decision-making, and organise his team efficiently for the adopted game plan. And he must psychologically prepare his players so that, when the team go out on to the field, no stone has been left unturned in the coach's quest for a top performance from the individuals who make up that team and the unit as a whole.

In conclusion, *Conditioning for Rugby League* is an essential guide for all coaches working with teams from 14 years upwards. Use it, question it, but above all ensure that those in your charge are indeed conditioned for Rugby League.

John Kear
RFL Coaching and Academy Executive
November 1996

CHAPTER 1

THE FITNESS SCENARIO

For nearly 70 years from the turn of the century, Great Britain were generally the dominant country in international Rugby League. However, the 1970s to mid-1980s saw a string of extremely one-sided Australian victories over their old enemy. Over the last two decades the Australians have elevated playing standards to previously unknown levels, and their approach to preparation and performance has been both progressive and extensive. There are a number of factors which have enabled the Australians to advance their performance to such an extent, and these include a favourable climate for training and much greater playing numbers than in Great Britain. "League" is the number one winter sport in New South Wales and Queensland, where it enjoys popularity akin to soccer in England.

With this in mind, Larder (1985) analysed the success of Australian Rugby League. He was particularly interested in the training methods utilised by the top clubs who, he found, had during the late 1970s and early 1980s adopted many training ideas from American football. He witnessed highly conditioned and athletic Rugby League players in the southern hemisphere who were better prepared for play, and who contrasted sharply with their British equivalents languishing in relatively poor physical condition.

Larder (1988) accurately highlighted the root of the problem in stating that, during the previous decade, many British coaches had failed to prepare their players physically. In particular, they had neglected to study modern developments in strength, speed and power training. The values of a base level of endurance had been underestimated, and flexibility had also not received due attention. Few coaches displayed any knowledge of the "principles" of training, and most either completely ignored fitness or simply prolonged their sessions until players were exhausted.

Most players' attitudes to training were the same as the coaches; basically, there was little or no structure to training. Few clubs provided adequate facilities for strength development, and many players even felt that strength training was not essential for Rugby League. The "stamina" sessions at many clubs consisted largely of touch rugby, which is a physically demanding yet very specific sport where there are no collisions. There was little understanding of the relevance of psychology to sport, and even less practice of mental skills. Hence it can be seen that British Rugby League players at the highest level had neither the opportunity nor the desire to prepare themselves either physically or psychologically for competition at that level.

Not surprisingly, British standards fell far behind those of the antipodeans. After winning at Bradford in 1978, Great Britain lost the next 15 matches against Australia. During this ten-year period they also lost six times to New Zealand. Oxley (1985) stated that 1980 was the year when Britain's international standing reached its lowest ebb. The general consensus of opinion cited "lack of fitness" as the major reason.

An attempt was made to arrest the decline and remedy the poor condition of the players with the appointment in 1982 of Rod McKenzie from Carnegie College, Leeds, the Rugby Football League's fitness consultant. He designed weight training routines and running schedules at Carnegie in 1983 in preparation for the 1984 Lions tour to Australasia. At first McKenzie had a difficult job, as few took seriously this new technical approach to training. He attempted to highlight the players' weaknesses in relation to the game and tried to design training sessions to meet the specific demands placed on the player during a game.

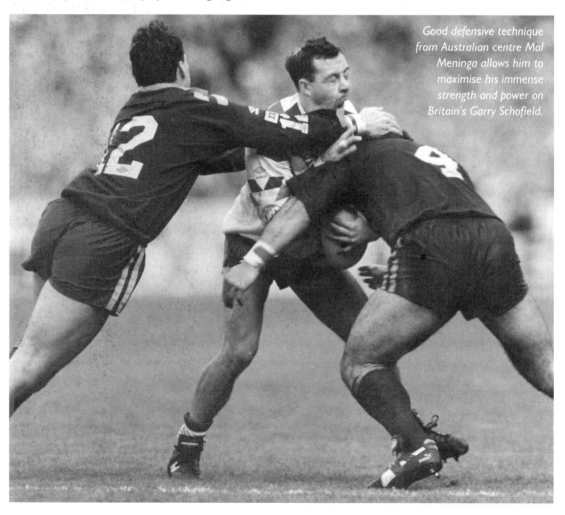

Good defensive technique from Australian centre Mal Meninga allows him to maximise his immense strength and power on Britain's Garry Schofield.

McKenzie could see the way Rugby League had to progress. Unfortunately, he had little supporting evidence regarding the exact demands of the game. This lack of information meant that it was practically impossible for him to implement his plans in a manner which specifically reproduced game situations. The 1984 Ashes series was lost 3–0, but at least the gravity of the situation was now recognised.

Coaches and players began to understand and appreciate the need for a more holistic approach to a Rugby League international. The next step by the Rugby Football League was to follow the

Simon Haughton, one of the new breed of fast and powerful youngsters, in action for England in the Fiji 9s of 1994.

Australian lead and study American football. Larder (1985) carried out a major investigation into the Los Angeles Rams, analysing all aspects of their organisation. The Great Britain team's preparation began to assume a more scientific basis and, in 1987, the international squad started attending assessment sessions at the Human Performance Centre at Lilleshall. Here, tests have been administered to determine strength, speed, aerobic endurance, anaerobic capacity, power and flexibility. The recommendations from these tests have been implemented into training programmes and have contributed to the renaissance of British Rugby League.

One of the results of this progress was that, in the third Test at the Sydney Football Stadium in 1988, an understrength British team with a wide range of age and experience beat Australia 26–12. Great Britain won again in 1990, by the margin of 19–12 at Wembley Stadium in that year's first Test. In the next series in Australia in 1992, Britain won the second Test 33–10. However, despite these memorable victories, all of these series were lost by two matches to one, and the Stones Bitter Rugby League World Cup final at Wembley in October 1992 was also won by Australia, 10–6.

Martin Offiah, formerly of Wigan – speed personified.

Andrew Farrell, England's youngest ever captain, puts the full force of his frame into a collision in the 1996 World 9s.

There can be no doubt that the differences between the two nations are not what they were. On the recent 1992 tour to Australia, Great Britain's midweek side were extremely successful against quality opposition, as well as the same year's World Cup final being a very close affair. Unfortunately, this may yet be something of a false dawn. The crux of the issue is that, while Britain can field several players of true world standing, Australia can arguably field several teams of that class – as was demonstrated in the 1995 Halifax Rugby League Centenary World Cup. The speed and intensity of the Australian domestic competition far surpasses that of the English league. Physically, with the majority of players, a gulf still exists.

The current situation

The present problem is not insurmountable. At the moment, the Australians have a greater number of dedicated players and coaches. British coaches have still to realise that recent advances in sport have been greater than in many other walks of life. The appliance of science has brought improved training methods and modern technology to Rugby League, but these need to be utilised to a still greater extent.

As Davey (1988) indicated:

"For a footballer to reach his maximum potential he needs the assistance not only of a coach, but a small team of sport scientists including an exercise physiologist and sport psychologist."

In essence, the sport needs a clearer picture of exactly what to test and train for. It may be that much of the training undertaken by players is unnecessary. Time may be better spent on more specific match activities. Larder (1988) described general physiological principles and the role they play in Rugby League. He reiterated the point made by McKenzie in 1983 that the coach must test each of his players physically and, from the results, plan individual training programmes specific to their needs and to the role they are expected to play in a game.

It does seem that, for nearly ten years, British coaches have been highlighting the need for specific training, but at no point has a concerted effort been made to adopt this principle. With this information in mind, a research programme was commissioned by the Rugby Football League and commenced at Liverpool University. The purpose of this study was to analyse the key aspects of performance in Rugby League football, and to investigate the key determinants of success. This research endeavoured to discover what is missing from and what should be added to the preparation sessions of Rugby League players; to provide information that could for the first time allow Rugby League players to prepare specifically and more thoroughly for Rugby League football, on the basis of sound evidence.

The data was derived from two methods:

- *Attempts were made to obtain data from the best players in the British game. This had not been done before and, as such, the country had wasted much of the talent at its disposal. This is because élite players had been allowed to disappear from the game without leaving any documentation of their thoughts and opinions on the sport they played;*

- *A major match analysis programme was carried out which studied all the playing positions over numerous games, so as to develop regularity and allow for variables such as the opposition, conditioning, and the importance of the game.*

CHAPTER 2

THE ANALYSIS PROJECT

A questionnaire was administered to 34 Great Britain Rugby League players about several aspects of the game and, in particular, fitness. The players were asked which aspects of the game caused them most fatigue. Some players gave several responses, and these are shown in the table below.

Fatigue is caused by:

Being tackled	47%
Tackling	32%
Covering/supporting	26%
Quick play-the-ball	15%
Other	15%

The overriding cause of fatigue appears to be related to the collision. Physical contact with another player is very demanding: the players stated that making consecutive tackles is especially tiring, while absorbing the impact of several defenders is harder than a long sprint. The players were also asked how fatigue affects their performance, and their responses are shown below.

Fatigue leads to:

Less power, speed/strength	38%
More mistakes	32%
Slower reactions	26%
Loss of concentration	21%
Less support	12%

The main problem with fatigue, therefore, is that it reduces a player's power, i.e., his ability to be strong and fast. Tired players are unable to accelerate as quickly and collide with the same intensity in attack and defence. As these factors are essential in Rugby League, it can be seen that fatigue is a problem in that it causes a general deterioration in performance.

Most players are aware of this and, when asked what their main playing strengths are, only 18% said work rate, i.e., the ability to work at high intensity for the full duration of the game. A significant proportion of players felt that they had good strength but were not able to display this for 80 minutes, while 56% of players required more speed, both for running in open field and into the collision.

It was therefore recognised that many players were interested and/or concerned about the fitness side of the sport. A video analysis project was then implemented to study the physical requirements for playing Rugby League. This centred on what was felt to be the critical element of play – the collision. Players were individually filmed during British first division games, and an analysis was also done of the first Test in Sydney in 1992 between Australia and Great Britain. Using a slow-motion video (50 frames/second) the researcher was able carefully and accurately to note by hand the players' activities.

The aspects of offence that were analysed were:

1. *The mode of forward locomotion that the ball-carrier was in when he took possession of the ball (i.e., walking, jogging, striding or sprinting), and the duration of that movement in 100ths of a second;*

2. *The mode of forward locomotion that the ball-carrier was in when he collided with the defenders (i.e., walking, jogging, striding or sprinting), and the duration of that movement in 100ths of a second;*

3. *The part of the ball-carrier's body where the defenders collide with him (i.e., front upper, rear upper, front lower, rear lower);*

4. *The number of defenders involved in the tackle;*

5. *The distance moved in the collision, in metres. This was either plus (towards the defenders' goal-line), or minus (towards the ball-carrier's own goal-line), and represented the distance that the ball moved from the first contact with the first defender to the position where the ball was subsequently played;*

6. *The duration of the collision in 100ths of a second. This was divided into two parts. The first part was an analysis of how long the player could remain on his feet in the collision, and was recorded from the first contact with the first defender to the point when the ball-carrier's upper body hit the ground. The second part was analysis of how quickly the ball-carrier could restart play, from the moment his upper body made contact with the ground to the point when he subsequently played the ball with his foot;*

7. *The result of the offensive collision: was the attacker held on his feet or grounded?*

Super League action at its best in the first ever London-Paris clash of the capitals.

The aspects of defence that were analysed were:

1. The mode of locomotion that the defender was in when he collided with the ball-carrier (i.e., standing, walking, jogging, striding or sprinting), and the duration of that movement in 100ths of a second;

2. The distance moved in the collision, in metres, from first contact to last contact;

3. The duration of the collision in 100ths of a second, from first contact to last contact;

4. The result of the defensive collision: was the defender standing or grounded, and on top of or below the ball-carrier?

A summary of the findings from the Test match analysis shows that the Australian players were stronger and faster than the British players. This is because the data shows that:

- The Australian attackers ran on to passes more quickly than the British;

- The Australian attackers approached the collision more quickly than the British;

- The Australian attackers remained on their feet in the collision longer than the British;

- The Australian attackers made more ground towards their opponents' goal-line in the collision than the British;

- The Australian attackers regained their feet after the tackle more quickly than the British;

- The Australian attackers required more defenders to halt their progress than the British;

- The Australian defenders approached the defensive collision with greater speed than the British;

- The Australian defenders lost less ground in the collision than the British.

It therefore appears that physical prowess played a major part in determining the result of that particular Test match. The following recommendations are thus necessary:

Strength, speed, power and endurance are prerequisites to being a top Rugby League player. Their development is a priority.

CHAPTER 3

BASIC EXERCISE PHYSIOLOGY

There are three different kinds of muscle responsible for movement:

Cardiac – this is the durable tissue that forms the walls and portions of the heart. These fibres cannot be prevented from contracting and do so rhythmically, without receiving impulses from the brain, at an average rate of 72 beats per minute.

Smooth – this muscle is located in the walls of internal organs such as blood vessels and intestines. It contracts involuntarily, is very sensitive to temperature and chemical stimuli, and has considerable ability for sustained contraction.

Skeletal/striated – this is the focal type of muscle in movement. The skeletal system provides the levers against which the muscles apply force. This muscle has special characteristics:

1. *Excitability* – it is able to receive and respond to a stimulus;

2. *Contractability* – it can change shape, usually becoming shorter and thicker as a result of a stimulus;

3. *Extensibility* – it can be stretched beyond its normal length;

4. *Elasticity* – it returns to its normal length when the stretching force is eliminated.

During the process of movement different muscles act in different ways:

● Agonist – this is a muscle which causes a movement and is sometimes known as the prime mover. For example, in the arm curl, the biceps are the agonists.

● Antagonist – this is a muscle which would oppose a movement if it contracted. Therefore, in order to permit free movement, it must relax and lengthen. As an example, the triceps are antagonists in the arm curl.

● Fixator – this is a muscle which contracts to prevent unwanted movement. For example, muscles of the back work in this manner to maintain posture and body position.

● Regulator – this is a muscle which controls a movement caused by the force of gravity, which happens when, for example, lowering a heavy weight.

● Neutraliser – this contracts to prevent the unwanted action of another muscle while permitting the desired action of that muscle. This occurs, for example, in the stomach when sitting up.

● Synergist – this works in a complex manner to assist in movement and make the actions of the agonists stronger.

Muscle Contraction

A muscle fibre is a cylindrical cell which has repeating dark and light bands – so giving it the name "striated muscle". The striations are due to more basic structural components called myofibrils which run the length of the muscle. Each myofibril is composed of a long series of sarcomeres, which are the fundamental units of muscle contraction. The sarcomere is composed of a thick filament called myosin and a thin filament called actin, and is bound by the Z line. A muscle shortens by the thin filaments sliding over the thick filaments, or by the Z lines moving towards one another. This is accomplished by tiny cross bridges extending from the thicker myosin filaments to the thinner actin filaments. The cross bridges reach out, make contact, and pull like oars. This happens throughout the whole muscle, and the combined action of thousands of fibres causes movement.

What makes the muscle contract?

When a load is placed on a muscle it is detected by nerves, and an appropriate number of fibres are stimulated to contract. What happens is that a nerve impulse travels from the spine to the junction between the nerve and muscle, and when it arrives there it initiates electrical activity in the muscle fibre. This electrical current travels inside the muscle and causes the release of calcium, which opens up sites on the thin filaments (actin) to which the thick filaments (myosin) attach themselves. This enables the muscle to contract.

For muscles to work like this they need energy, and this is obtained from food. The energy contained within food is used by the body to generate high-energy molecules that are used up in the process of muscle contraction. The actual molecule that muscles need in order to work is called adenosine triphosphate (ATP). Millions of ATP molecules are used during the process of muscle contraction, which reduces ATP to ADP, or adenosine diphosphate. The ATP store can only last for two to three seconds, and this must be restored immediately for muscles to work continuously and effectively.

ATP can be restored by three pathways, and an understanding of these biological systems which provide the metabolic basis for specific exercise and training is important for efficient conditioning programmes.

The systems are:

1. **The Phosphocreatine System**. When the level of ATP falls, a system is activated whereby a further phosphate group is immediately donated to allow contraction to continue. During intense muscular activity, this system may only be able to restore ATP for five to six seconds. This system allows short bursts of high-intensity activity such as sprinting or heavy/low repetition weight training. It is also working at the start of any activity.

2. **Anaerobic Glycolysis (Lactic acid) system**. When a situation occurs whereby ATP must be restored at a high rate after the phosphocreatine system has been exhausted, the muscle's carbohydrate stores (i.e., glycogen) are broken down rapidly to produce ATP. This occurs when training is quite intense. The process by which this happens is called anaerobic glycolysis, and this leads to the formation of lactic acid as a by-product. The accumulation of lactate (salt of lactic acid) has a role in muscle fatigue, which occurs if there is insufficient oxygen in the muscle. The exercise intensity which causes this rapid rise in lactate levels is about threequarters of maximum in trained athletes, whereas it is only a half of maximum in untrained individuals. Weight training and interval sprints both lead to the body adapting so as to increase the amount of resting glycogen, which makes this system more efficient. However, glycogen stores must be adequately replaced after exercise (see Chapter 8).

3. **Aerobic System**. If sufficient oxygen is available in the muscle (which generally means that exercise intensity is lower), no lactic acid builds up, as waste products do not accumulate in the muscle.

In the presence of oxygen, the major way to produce ATP is to metabolise fat. This takes a certain amount of time to be broken down, but can supply energy for long-duration exercise.

The three energy systems differ in the intensity and duration of exercise for which they supply energy. Short, high-intensity weights and sprints use the phosphocreatine system, while long, low-intensity training such as a 30–40 minute run calls primarily on the aerobic system. At no time does only one system provide all the energy required, but the relative contribution of each is determined by the intensity of exercise. By employing the correct training principles we are able to improve the efficiency of all our energy systems.

CHAPTER 4

STRENGTH TRAINING

The Science

Strength is the ability of the body, or a segment of the body, to apply force. It has been shown that this can be improved with progressive resistance training. This is a form of exercise where the muscle is overloaded, meaning it must work against a force that it does not encounter in everyday life. This stress causes certain adaptations within the muscle, as a result of which it becomes stronger.

Central to that adaptation is the motor unit. This consists of the neurone, which is the nerve pathway from the brain to the muscle, and a collection of muscle fibres branching out from that neurone. The smaller the number of muscle fibres in a motor unit, the smaller the amount of force that the motor unit will produce when stimulated to contract. The motor unit of the eye contains ten muscle fibres, whereas the calf muscle has 1,000. Either all of the fibres in a motor unit contract or none of them contract, and this is known as the "all or none" law.

The fibres of a motor unit are scattered about the whole muscle, so total movement occurs but with varying degrees of force depending on the number of motor units recruited. This is what makes possible different levels of muscle contraction. For example, when picking up a light object such as a ball, only a small number of muscles are required. Therefore only a few motor units come into operation when receiving a ball. More muscles, however, are required to lift a heavy object such as a player, so more motor units are stimulated when preparing to tackle, meaning more force can be developed. Therefore, if a weak contraction is required, only weak signals are sent from the central nervous system but, for a strong contraction, the signal is carried by more motor neurones.

There are two types of fibres involved in the contraction process and they are served by different motor units. Slow-twitch fibres, known as Type 1, are used in low-intensity, long-duration activities such as walking or jogging, and cannot generate much force. They are slow to contract but contain a lot of blood and oxygen and can therefore contract for long periods. Fast-twitch fibres, or Type 2, are suited to high-intensity, short-duration work, and have the potential to generate much greater force. They contract quickly and relax quickly but have low levels of endurance. These fibres are divided into two types, Type 2a and Type 2b; of these, the former is recruited first, while the latter is only recruited when the body is called upon to apply extreme force.

The order in which motor units and therefore fibres are recruited is generally constant and, according to the size principle of motor neurones, the larger ones are more difficult to stimulate. Fast-twitch motor units are very large compared to slow-twitch motor units. Therefore, if a light weight is lifted, predominantly slow-twitch motor units are recruited. If the weight is increased or the speed increased, the fast-twitch motor units are added as more force is required.

The determining factor in whether to recruit fast-twitch motor units or not is the total amount of force necessary to perform the contraction. Fast-twitch fibres are somewhat stubborn, and will not be recruited unless every other fibre has been used. Therefore, to affect a muscle fibre permanently, the intensity must be very high.

There are four main ways that a muscle fibre can be affected:

1. An increase in strength

Weight training causes an increase in neural drive, which means that a stronger signal is sent from the brain causing the existing fibres to contract with more force. It also improves the synchronisation of the motor units, meaning that more fibres contract at the same time which leads to a greater production of force. A further aspect is that weight training with high loads teaches the muscle fibres to co-ordinate themselves better, which means that the relevant agonists, antagonists and synergists are appropriately activated. A programme of weights will increase both the capacity of the muscle to store energy and also the concentration of enzymes which enable muscles to generate high amounts of tension. Another major way in which weight training makes muscles strong is by reducing the inhibitions in the muscle, meaning that more fibres can respond to a stimulus. What this means is that the protective mechanisms within the muscle are overridden to a certain extent as the brain realises that, while the weight is heavy, it is not unduly dangerous.

How is this achieved in reality?
The player needs to perform several sets of a particular exercise with a very heavy weight. There should be a reasonably long rest in between sets e.g., two to three minutes, to allow a complete regeneration of the energy stores.

To become stronger, the player needs to recruit every single muscle fibre, which requires him to lift a weight which is over 80% of his maximum capability. The speed of the exercise should be moderate to slow, so that a massive amount of tension can be developed. A twelve-week programme to increase strength should consist of three or four exercises, and should be as follows.

Full descriptions of these exercises, and procedures for coaches and players to follow while training, can be found later in this chapter.

Weeks 1–6   Bench press, squats, upright rows, step-ups

Weeks 1–2   3-5 sets of 3–5 reps, *speed 402, rest = 3 minutes

Weeks 3–4   3-5 sets of 1–3 reps, *speed = 602, rest = 2 minutes 30 seconds

Weeks 5–6   3-5 sets of 5–8 reps, *speed = 302, rest = 2 minutes

Weeks 7–12 Dips, power cleans (performed quickly), military press, dead lift

Same sets, reps, speed and rest as in weeks 1 to 6

*Speed   1st number = seconds to move down;

               2nd number = seconds in between;

               3rd number = seconds to move up

---

2.   An increase in size

A prolonged period of muscular contraction increases the secretion of testosterone, which is released from the testes into the blood and travels to the skeletal muscle where it contributes to growth. Another hormone called growth hormone is also released when the rest periods are short and the next set is started before complete recovery has taken place. This stimulates muscle growth by promoting the transfer of amino acids from outside the cell to inside; thus inside the muscle there is an increase in the number of actin and myosin filaments. Although training causes an increase in the size of all fibre types, there is greater growth of the Type 2 fibres. This probably reflects a greater relative involvement of these high-threshold units than would occur in normal daily activity.

A further theory of growth is that lactic acid build-up during this type of training forces an extension of the capillary network to remove the waste products. This extension serves to bring in more nutrients and oxygen, allowing the muscle to work for longer which can promote muscle growth and facilitate greater repair after the session.

How is this achieved in reality?

The player needs to perform more repetitions than when training for strength, meaning that less resistance should be used. The higher number of repetitions prolongs the period of mechanical stress and metabolic cost.

Weeks 1–6	**Bench press, squats, upright rows, step-ups, other exercises of choice**
Weeks 1–2	3 sets of 10–12 reps, speed = 402, rest = 60 seconds
Weeks 3–4	4 sets of 8–10 reps, speed = 402, rest = 60 seconds
Weeks 5–6	3 sets of 12–15 reps, speed = 202, rest = 45 seconds
Weeks 7–12	**Dips, power cleans (performed quickly), military press, dead lift, other exercises of choice**
Same sets, reps, speed and rest as in weeks 1–6	

3. An increase in endurance

As muscle strength increases, fewer fibres are required to perform a given task, which means that the muscle can perform the task for longer. As previously mentioned, specific training can increase the energy stores within, and blood supply to, the muscle. Muscular endurance training will also increase the activity of certain enzymes which allow fibres to work for longer. There may also be a conversion of certain fast-twitch fibres to take on the qualities of slow-twitch fibres, which means that they will have more endurance.

To improve muscular endurance, the player needs to perform high repetitions of a particular exercise over several sets with very short rest periods in between. This can be done on specific exercises, for example, three sets of 30–40 bench press with 30 seconds' rest in between. However, a more popular and effective method of improving muscular endurance is circuit training.

This consists of a series of resistance exercises (10–15) arranged in sequence to work different body parts. For example:

Bench Press

Trunk Curl

Squats

Upright Rows

Back Raises

Leg Curls

Military Press

Sit-ups

Leg Extensions

Power Cleans

Circuit training will improve general cardiovascular fitness as well as specific muscular endurance, and can be done once a week, or grouped together three times a week in a four- to six-week period at the start of the season.

4.   An increase in power

Power is defined as work divided by time, or the rate of doing something. It combines force and velocity, and is therefore the product of multiplying strength by speed. One who is able to do more in the same unit of time has more power; a person who can move 100kg one metre in one second has more power than a person who can do the same thing in two seconds. It is extremely difficult to increase one's speed of movement as it was generally set down at birth along with the number of fibres. However, more strength combined with the same speed does equal more power.

That said, a slow, heavy weights programme for strength may also be effective in increasing speed, as this type of training is effective at recruiting the fast-twitch fibres which are used in sprinting. But, at the same time, research shows that when working with a resistance of around 30–50 per cent of maximum the power output is greatest. It is therefore necessary to implement a programme with light weights wherein the player attempts to move as fast as possible.

WEEKS	SETS	REPS	SPEED	REST
3	3	20 (30 per cent of maximum)	0.5/0/0.5	90 secs
3	3	10 (50 per cent of maximum)	0.5/0/0.5	90 secs

To elicit the improvements in strength, size and endurance which have been discussed, there are several factors regarding this type of training that the coach must be aware of.

The length/tension relationship.

It is important to note that there is an optimum length at which muscles will generate most force (such as the half-way point on arm curls, or the point during a bench press where you feel strongest). This is the point at which the largest number of cross bridges are formed within the muscle, which means that maximum tension can be developed. At a lower position there are fewer cross bridges, and at a higher position there are too many filaments "in the way", both of which mean that the muscle is weaker. Many people avoid these optimum positions and only work through a partial range of motion, which is a mistake as the muscle does not get totally developed. Therefore the player must always work through the full range of movement.

The force/velocity relationship.

As the velocity of contraction increases, the force that is developed decreases. If the player has to bench press as much as possible in 0.5 seconds, he cannot do as much as if he is given four seconds. This force/velocity relationship is dependent on the rate that cross bridges can be formed, broken and reformed within the muscle. Since power is determined by the strength and speed of the shortening of the muscle, power output can therefore be improved by increasing either parameter. There is little evidence that training can improve the speed at which the muscle shortens, but strength work does yield significant results. There is no evidence that this will cause players to lose speed. The most effective approach is to vary both the speed of the exercise and the weights used.

The angle of pull.

A further cause of differences in a muscle's strength at different phases of its movement is the "angle of pull" of the muscle. A muscle's direction of pull is along its axis, with the resulting movement being transferred along the tendon. If the direction of pull is not directly in line with the resulting direction of movement of the bone, then the pull will be very inefficient. For example, with the arm curl, the direction of pull is initially upwards, yet the initial movement is forwards. This is inefficient. As flexion continues, the direction of pull and movement become similar. This is because the muscle is strongest in the mid-range.

The coach needs to be constantly aware of these three factors when coaching weights and bear them in mind when designing or altering his training programme. Successful manipulation of these throughout the year by variation will yield good results for all his players. There are three different methods that can be used to develop strength, size, endurance and power.

Isometric. This is where tension develops in the muscle, but there is no change in the length. Such exercises are normally performed against an immovable object such as a wall, a team-mate or an extremely heavy weight that cannot be moved. The contraction is held for a certain duration (five to ten seconds) and repeated several times. Strength gains have been noted using this method as well as increases in muscle size. This type of training has relevance to Rugby League as it has been shown to recruit fast-twitch fibres; also because it partially replicates the static component within the collision.

There are two types of isometric exercises, which are:

(a) Concentric. The player attempts to move an immovable object with maximum effort. The coach should choose for him exercises for both upper and lower body, and the load should be placed entirely on the muscles being targeted, with minimum strain being exerted on other muscles.

Isometric exercises for various body parts.

(b) Eccentric. With the aid of spotters, the player resists a weight which is greater than he can lift. Each set lasts for just over 15 seconds, during which the weight is lowered to be resisted at three different levels for five seconds each. It is then pressed explosively upwards with the assistance of the spotters.

Isokinetic. This is where the muscle contracts at a constant speed through the entire range of motion. Working against an isokinetic machine, the resistance cannot be accelerated, but any force which the player applies results in an equal reaction force. In theory, this means that the muscle is working to its maximum all the time. Improvements in muscle function are well documented with this type of training. Unfortunately, the equipment costs thousands of pounds, and so its relevance to Rugby League training is limited.

Isotonic. This is where the length of the muscle changes, but the external resistance remains the same, for example, when using free weights. The contraction can be concentric, wherein the muscle shortens; or eccentric, wherein the muscle lengthens. This is the preferred type of training for Rugby League, for several reasons:

1. Movements are free-standing and multi joint and can be accelerated, like the movements in many sports;

2. A large number of muscle groups and connective tissues are activated, which has a good effect on balance and co-ordination;

3. Specific exercises can be designed which replicate particular movements in particular sports;

4. There is a vast array of ways in which free weights can be used;

5. Free weights are relatively inexpensive and available to all;

6. Free weights are good for joint stability.

The Weights Room

The effective weights room needs good light, good ventilation, mirrors, and a supply of running water. Herein, the coach has considerable responsibility. In particular, he must ensure that:

1. There is sufficient space in the weights room;

2. The floor is even, firm and non-slip;

3. The players wear loose but warm clothing;

4. The players wear suitable training shoes, i.e., firm sole, good heel (tennis shoes are better than running shoes);

5. Belts, though not essential, should not be discouraged;

6. Chalk is available if required, to maintain a good grip;

7. All weights and stands are regularly checked for damage, and to ensure that collars are tight;

8. Players do not increase the weight they are lifting before consulting the coach;

9. There is a display of rules and advisory notes in the gym;

10. Mats are available to place under weights and to use for floor exercises;

11. Players are encouraged to keep records of their progress;

12. Weights are always returned to the racks and the gym tidied at the end of the session.

Teaching Principles

The coach should attempt to follow this sequence of instruction:

1. Name the exercise (concisely);

2. Name the major part of the body being exercised, avoiding Latin/technical terms;

3. Give a silent demonstration in good style – be brief, but do two or three repetitions with the players watching from different angles;

4. Describe the technique briefly, but in detail, from start to finish;

5. Direct the player to the start position, and indicate the number of repetitions required;

6. Coach and encourage, picking out only one or two points to praise or improve.

It is generally better to correct major faults at the end of the set so as not to comment at the wrong time. The coach should then demonstrate again the correct method, show the incorrect method that the player was doing, then repeat the correct method. The coach should always be positive and supportive.

The Spotter

Players should always train in pairs, with one exercising and one "spotting". The spotter should be of a similar size and weight, and is there to assist, not to take over. He should ensure that the collars are tight and that the bar is evenly positioned. There must be a clear and known signal from the exerciser if he needs the spotter's help.

Breathing

It is important always to breathe out during the exertion part of an exercise. At no point should the player hold his breath, as this can cause problems with blood pressure.

The Exercises

Total Body Exercises

1. Power Clean

This is a total body exercise, developing the muscles of the legs, hips, back, arms and shoulders simultaneously, which improves synchronisation and co-ordination. A major component of this exercise is hip rotation, which is a key element in running and jumping. This exercise should be done early in the workout when the player is fresh.

1.   The bar is grasped with an overhand grip, hands slightly wider than shoulder width apart, with the elbows out, shoulders over the bar, body weight on the toes, but heels still in contact with the floor.

2.	The shins should be touching the bar, with the feet a shoulder width apart, and toes pointing slightly out.

3.	The knees should be bent, the back held straight at a 45° angle, and the chest out over the bar.

4.	The bar is eased off the floor using the legs and hips, keeping both the back and the arms straight. The hips and shoulders go up together with a feeling of driving the legs through the floor. The bar is kept close to the shins.

5.	The knees are then moved back slightly so that the bar can keep moving up in a straight line. They are pushed back under the bar after it has passed, and the weight continues upwards close to the thighs.

6.	The bar is now pulled up forcibly. The legs are extended, and the player rises on to his toes trying to get the bar as high as possible with only a very slight bend of the arms.

7.	The player must then get under the bar by bending at the knees. (He may move his feet slightly wider for balance.) The bar should finish at collar bone level and the elbows are held high. There should have been little, if any, movement of the bar at this point; the wrists should simply rotate.

8.	The bar is then lowered to hip level and returned to the floor by bending at the knees and hips while keeping the back straight.

2. High Pull

This exercise develops the muscles of the arms, shoulders and back.

1.	The player holds the bar with an overhand grip in the mid-thigh position.

2.	From here he bends slightly at the knee and, on extension, the bar is pulled as high and as fast as possible while remaining close to the body.

3.	The hips are pulled in and upward, and the player should rise on to his toes.

4.	The elbows and shoulders also rise upward, thus utilising the back and trapezius muscles in the finishing pull, which takes the bar up to neck height.

3. Push Press

This exercise develops the muscles of the arms and shoulders.

1.	The player grasps the bar with an overhand grip, hands shoulder width apart, with the bar at the top of the chest.

2. The wrists should be cocked backwards, and the elbows up and slightly outwards.

3. The back should be straight, abdominals taut, and the head up.

4. Bend at the knees and the hips, push the bar overhead with a full extension of the body.

5. The bar is returned to the start position with a slight knee bend.

Leg Exercises

1. Back Squat

This exercise develops the muscles of the legs, hips and back.

1. The feet should be positioned slightly wider than a shoulder width apart, and the toes slightly pointed out.

2. The bar is rested across the upper back and the back of the shoulders, with the hands placed evenly on the bar slightly wider than shoulder width apart.

3. The chest should be kept up and out, head up, and eyes looking straight ahead.

4. The player then descends under control by bending at the hips, knees and ankles.

5. The knees should be kept over the toes, with the buttocks going back.

6. The player squats to a position where his thighs are parallel to the floor, keeping his back straight all the time.

7. He then drives back up to the start position, remaining under control, by pushing "through the floor". There should be no forward lean. The head should remain up, chest out, and shoulders back. If the heels raise from the floor, this indicates a lack of flexibility or poor technique; to correct this, the player should work at ankle stretches and practise the exercise without the weight during his warm-up.

2. Dead Lift

This exercise develops the muscles of the legs, hips, back and shoulders.

1. The player should stand with feet a shoulder width apart, toes pointing slightly out, and the bar touching his shins.

2. The bar is held with an alternate grip, one hand under and one over, slightly wider than shoulder width apart. The player should make sure to change hands for each set.

3. The arms should be straight, elbows gently touching the legs, head up, chest up and out, hips low, and thighs parallel to the floor.

4.   The bar is lifted slowly by extending the legs and hips.

5.   The arms and back should be kept straight, and the bar pulled close to the body.

6.   The bar is raised until the legs are locked and the shoulders are in line with the body.

7.   The bar is then lowered by bending at the hips and knees.

8.   During the descent, the arms and back should be kept straight, with the weight even over both feet, and the bar close to the legs.

3. Step-ups

This exercise develops the muscles of the legs and hips.

1.   The player stands with one foot on the bench (so that a right angle is created at the knee) and the other on the floor.

2.   The weight should rest across the shoulders, as in the back squat.

3.   From this position, the player drives up using only the leg on the bench (lead leg) so that both feet finish on the bench.

4.   The player then returns to the start position, with the emphasis remaining on the lead leg, and repeats the movement. Change legs when required.

5.   The upper body should be kept upright at all times.

4. Lunges

This exercise develops the thigh region, and strengthens the hips and lower back.

1. The player grasps the bar with an overhand grip, hands slightly wider than shoulder width apart.

2. He positions the bar in a balanced position on the shoulders at the back of the neck, lifts the chest up and out, and pulls the shoulder blades towards each other.

3. To begin the exercise, he takes an exaggerated step directly forward with one leg, keeping the knee and foot aligned and the toes pointing straight ahead.

4. He plants the lead foot squarely on the ground and flexes the lead knee, slowly lowering the trail knee to a position slightly above the floor.

5. He keeps the torso vertical by "sitting back" on the trailing leg, and keeps the lead knee directly over the lead foot, without bouncing.

6. He then forcefully pushes off with the lead leg, maintaining body position, and brings the lead foot back to a position next to the trailing foot. The exercise is then repeated, using the other leg to lead.

5. Leg Press

This exercise develops the front and rear thigh muscles and strengthens the hips.

1. This can be done on either a seated or lying machine. In either case it is essential that the back is supported, while the feet should be a shoulder width apart, pointing straight ahead. There will also be handles for the player to grasp.

2. The starting position is with the legs flexed at the knee at an angle slightly greater than $90°$.

3. From here the player pushes against the platform and extends the legs, avoiding forceful locking-out of the knees.

4. The weight is then returned slowly to the starting position.

6. Leg Extension

 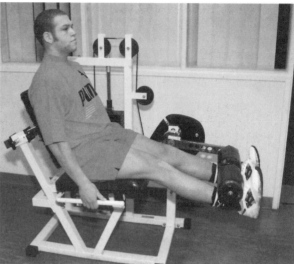

This exercise develops the upper muscles in the front of the legs.

1. The player assumes a seated position on the machine, with his back straight, and places his feet in the appropriate position.

2. He then fully extends his legs, holds the position for a moment, then bends his legs slowly to return to the start position.

3. The weight must remain under control at all times.

7. Leg Curls

This exercise develops the muscles at the back of the upper leg.

1. The player lies face downwards on a leg curl machine, with legs fully extended.

2. From this position he brings his ankles up to the buttocks as far as he can.

3. He then returns to the start position, with full extension of the legs.

8. Calf Raises

This exercise develops the muscles at the rear of the lower leg.

1. The bar is placed at the base of the neck, while the feet – which are hip width apart – are on a slight raise (approximately 4–5 cm).

2. The player pushes up on his toes as high as possible in a controlled manner, maintaining thigh and lower leg position.

3. He then descends until his heels return to the floor.

9. Hip Adduction

This exercise develops the leg muscles.

1. The physiotherapist's therapeutic band should be fixed to an immovable object at ankle level next to the player's right leg.

2. The player then stands upright approximately 50cm away, with the other end of the band attached to his right ankle.

3. From here, while balancing himself on one leg, he sweeps his right leg across the midline of his body.

4. He then returns the leg to the starting position.

5. There should be minimal strain from other parts of the body.

10. Hip Abduction

This is similar to adduction, but the player now works the outside of the leg.

Trunk Exercises

1. Trunk Curl

This exercise develops the muscles of the abdominals.

1. The player lies on his back with knees bent, feet close to the buttocks, and arms crossed over the chest.

2. From this position the player attempts to curl his shoulders on to his chest, but does not sit up.

3. When he has reached his furthest point he returns to the start.

2. Reverse Abdominal Curl

This exercise develops the muscles of the hips and stomach.

1. The player lies on his back with legs bent, knees tucked into the chest, and arms to the sides.

2. From this position he extends his legs at a 45° angle, keeping his back flat on the floor.

3. He then returns his legs back into his chest, raising the buttocks slightly off the floor.

3. Chinnie Sit-up

This exercise develops the muscles of the hips and abdominals.

1. The player lies on his back with legs outstretched, arms flexed at the elbow, hands on the sides of the head, and elbows tucked into the chest.

2. He brings his left knee into the chest by flexing the and raising the upper body slightly to push the right elbow outside the left knee.

3. He returns to the start position, and repeats with the opposite leg and elbow.

4. Back Raises

This exercise develops the muscles of the back, and can be done either on a special machine, or on a high bench with a partner holding the player's legs.

1. The player starts face down on the apparatus, with his upper body over the edge from the waist up.

2. With his back straight, shoulders back, chest out, and arms behind the head, the player bends at the hip and lowers his torso to a position where it is perpendicular to the floor.

3. From here he returns to the start and to a straight back.

4. There should be no hyperextension (i.e., arching the back past parallel), but weights can be added for advanced trainers.

Upper Body Exercises

1. Bench Press

This exercise develops the muscles of the upper body.

1. The player lies on the bench with the shoulders, back and buttocks in contact with the bench and the knees bent, with feet to the sides and flat on the floor.

2. The bar is grasped with an overhand grip, hands slightly wider than shoulder width apart.

3. The bar is raised off the stands by pushing with the arms and locking the elbows. The bar should be stabilised above the chin.

4. From this position the player lowers the bar in an arc to the chest.

5. He then drives the bar back to the start position, i.e., above the chin.

6. There should be no arch or twist of the back, and no movement of the legs.

7. The bar should be returned to the stands in a controlled manner.

2. Incline Bench Press

This exercise develops the upper chest, shoulders and arms.

1. This can be done on a Smith's machine or free-weights bench with bar or dumb bells, and the angle of incline should be approximately 45°, although this can be varied.

2. The technique is the same as is used for the flat bench press, except that the player should lower the bar to his upper chest/collarbone area.

3. Dumb-bell Flys

This exercise develops the muscles of the upper chest, shoulders and upper arms.

 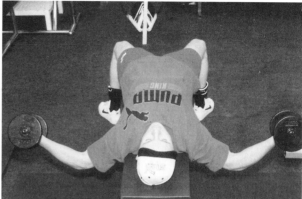

1. The player lies on his back on a bench, holding dumb-bells vertically upwards.

2. He then lowers his arms out to the sides in a controlled manner, with a slight bend of the elbow.

3. When the player feels an "open chest", he returns his arms to the start position.

4. Military Press

This exercise develops the muscles of the shoulders, arms and back, and can be performed either standing or sitting. The bar should be passed to the player by two spotters.

1. The player grasps the bar with an overhand grip, hands slightly wider than shoulder width apart, with the bar at the top of the chest.

2. The wrists should be straight and tight, but not fully extended, and the elbows should stay under the bar.

3. The back should be straight, abdominals taut, and head up.

4. The bar is pushed up straight overhead by extending the arms, while keeping the back straight.

5. From this position the bar is lowered again to the top of the chest.

5. Dumb-bell Raise
SIDE

This exercise develops the side and rear muscles of the shoulder region.

1. The player stands upright with his feet a shoulder width apart.

2. The dumb-bells are held with an overhand grip at the side of the thighs.

3. From here the arms are raised outwards while remaining extended, until they reach shoulder level from where they are returned to the starting position.

4. The body should be held as static as possible.

FRONT

This exercise develops the front shoulder region.

1. The starting position for this exercise is in front of the thighs.

2. From here the arms are raised to the front while remaining extended, until they reach shoulder level from where they are returned to the starting position.

6. Dips

This exercise develops the muscles of the shoulders, arms and chest.

 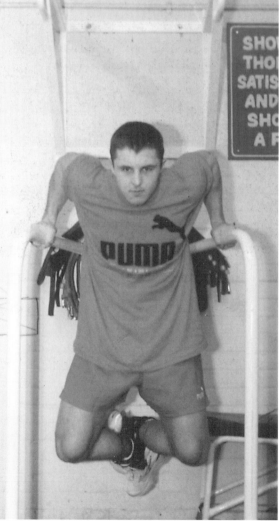

1. The player lifts himself on to the parallel bars, placing the palms of his hands slightly wider than shoulder width apart.

2. The player then lowers himself until his elbow angle is around 90°.

3. From this position he returns to the start by extending his elbows again.

4. Resistance can be added via a weights belt if required. This will be necessary for strength development.

7. Upright Rows

This exercise develops the muscles of the arms, back and shoulders.

1. The bar is held with an overhand grip, with hands four to six inches apart.

2. It is then raised close to the body by bending at the elbows and wrists until the bar is at chin level and the elbows are high.

3. From here the bar is returned to the start position.

8. Arm Curls

This exercise develops the muscles of the arms and shoulders.

1. The bar is held with an underhand grip, with the feet slightly wider than a shoulder width apart.

2. The bar is then lifted in an arc to shoulder level, keeping the elbows close to the body.

3. It is then returned to the start position, with no hip or back movement.

9. Sprint Curls

This exercise develops the muscles of the shoulders, upper chest, back and arms.

1. The player stands with his feet a shoulder width apart, holding dumb-bells in either hand.

2. He then simulates the arm action of a sprinter while holding the dumb-bells, performing the exercise as dynamically as possible.

10. Lat Pull-Downs

This exercise develops the muscles of the upper back and arms.

1. The player grasps the bar with an overhand grip, hands slightly wider than shoulder width apart, with the arms fully extended.

2. Keeping the torso erect, he pulls the bar down towards the neck.

3. As the bar touches the base of the neck he allows the arms slowly to extend fully.

11. Seated Row

This exercise develops the upper and central muscles of the back and arms.

1. The player assumes a seated position facing the machine.

2. He places his feet on the machine's foot supports and positions his torso perpendicular to the floor.

3. He then slightly flexes at the knees and fully extends his arms, holding the bar or handle with an overhand grip.

4. He then pulls the bar or handle into the chest/upper abdomen while keeping the body erect and stationary.

5. As the bar touches the chest, the player allows it to move away from the body slowly, controlling it by maintaining body position and keeping the arms next to the ribs.

12. Tricep Extension

This exercise develops the muscles at the rear of the upper arm.

1. Facing the machine, the player grasps the bar with an overhand grip.

2. He establishes an upright body position, either knelt or stood, with the feet a shoulder width apart and knees slightly flexed.

3. He moves the bar down to a position where his elbows are next to his torso and his forearms parallel to the floor.

4. From this starting position he pushes the bar down until the arms fully extend.

5. He then allows the bar to rise slowly under control while maintaining an erect body position.

6.   He stops the bar when his forearms are parallel to the floor.

13. Forearm Curls

This exercise develops the muscles of the forearm.

1.   With the forearms resting on a bench or the player's knees, the bar is held with the wrists hyperextended, using an underhand grip.

2.   The player then lifts the weight by flexing the wrists and fingers as far as possible.

CHAPTER 5

SPEED

Speed is the quality which allows one to perform a given movement in a very short period of time. It is the capacity to move a limb, or a part of the body's lever system, with great velocity.

The development of speed depends on several factors. Good technique is critical, as athletes can only run as fast as their technique allows. A key element is the stride length: it has been shown that, on the whole, faster runners have longer stride lengths. If a player can increase this without reducing the rate of leg movement, then he will become quicker. Stride length is made of three distances:

1. The distance from the body's centre of gravity to the toe of the take-off foot when it leaves the ground. This is dependent on the length of the legs and the flexibility of the hip joint.

2. The horizontal distance which the body's centre of gravity travels through the air, which is dependent on the speed, height and angle of release of the body from the ground, plus air resistance.

3. The distance which the toe of the lead foot lands ahead of the body's centre of gravity. It is ideal for this to be approximately 25cms.

A technically correct runner will be a more efficient runner. A good technique is one where the arms are relaxed with the shoulders down. Raised shoulders create tension in the upper neck and back. The hands should be relaxed, with the arms at a loose 90° angle and moving straight back like pistons to thrust the runner forward. When driving forward the hands should come no higher than chin level, and not across the body. There should be no twist of the upper body. The face should be relaxed, with eyes looking straight ahead.

A high knee lift is crucial. The front thigh should come up to a position parallel to the ground, which will allow the rear leg to extend fully. This maximises the force output from the lower leg muscles. The front leg must then accelerate "down" to the floor, while the heel of the rear leg follows through close to the buttock – the closer the better, so that this leg has to move through less space to reach the drive position. All the time, the trunk should be upright with only a slight forward lean.

The ability to stimulate the correct units to "fire" the fastest muscles is also crucial to fast running, and this depends on the extent to which the central nervous system can make quick alternating moves, i.e., how many fast-twitch fibres one possesses. Some top sprinters have as much as 90 per cent fast-twitch fibres within their leg muscles. In many respects you cannot alter what you are born with; it is said that top sprinters are born, not made. There are, however, two types of fast-twitch fibres, as was stated before. With training, it may be possible to increase the proportion of the "faster" type.

Biochemistry is also important for speed, development, in particular the extent to which the muscle has the correct energy supplies and how well developed is the energy system which allows muscles to react. Similarly will power plays a part, that is, the extent to which a player wants to be faster. Gains will be very limited, and one must be persistent over a number of years to see real improvements.

Training

Of all the methods of speed development, running drills are the most accepted way to improve. Examples of these are:

1. **Butt-kickers**. The upper leg does not move much, but the lower leg flicks back at speed to touch the buttock. Speed back down to the floor is crucial.

2. **High knees**. With an upright upper body, the player works on bringing his knees as high as possible very quickly. The heel should be tucked right under the buttock.

3. **Skipping**. This should be done with the emphasis on full extension of the take-off leg, keeping the knee of the support leg high, the thigh parallel to the floor, and driving back well with the elbows.

4. **Toe walk**. To strengthen the ankles and calf muscles, the player should try to walk as tall as possible on his toes, rather than just the balls of his feet.

5. **Fast arms**. While standing still, the player should work the arm through the full range of motion as quickly as possible.

6. **Fast feet**. Over a short distance of 10–15 metres, the player makes contact with the ground as many times as possible, with minimal knee lift and the emphasis on fast arms and legs.

7. **Alternate drive**. The player jogs forward slowly with very small strides and performs every third arm and leg movement as quickly as possible with good technique, i.e., high knee lift and full elbow drive backwards.

Sprinting

No fatigue should be allowed to develop in speed training, because it is essential that the nervous system is in a state of optimal excitement. There should be considerable rest in between repetitions, and even longer between sets. Every sprint should be done at maximal effort. There are a vast array of sprints which can be done, but the emphasis must always be on quality not quantity.

For maximum speed development, it may be best for the player to sprint in spikes on a track, but the volume of training must be increased gradually. He should also undertake a considerable amount of work on grass.

Hill running is another alternative. The player can do uphill running (2–10 degrees incline) for 10–40 metres or downhill sprinting. The latter type of assisted running is good because it develops fast limb movements which can increase muscle excitability and improve co-ordination.

Weight Training

This has been dealt with in the chapter on strength development. It is an integral part of any speed programme; look at Linford Christie. The more force that a runner can impart against the ground, the faster he will move.

Resistance Running

Methods such as towing weight sleds and running with weighted vests may improve speed, but should only be done after consultation with an expert.

Plyometrics Training

A popular and very successful method of becoming quicker is plyometrics. This type of training is designed to bridge the gap between strength and speed, to improve the explosive action of leaping from one foot to another which is known as sprinting. The main objective of plyometrics is to convert elastic energy provided by body weight and force of gravity during the eccentric (i.e., lengthening) phase into an equal and opposite force during the concentric (i.e., shortening) phase. It is basically resistance training which involves an interaction between the muscles and the central nervous system which decreases the time between lengthening and shortening of the muscle.

It is essential that the time delay between the eccentric and concentric phase is as short as possible, so that the muscle can utilise as much energy as possible. This is known as the strength reflex, and is a result of the activity of muscle spindles. These are the movement receptors in the muscle, and they detect changes in muscle length and are particularly sensitive to how rapidly the length is changing (i.e., stretching). The sensory endings of the muscle spindles are coiled around muscle fibres. When the muscle is rapidly stretched, as when hopping or jumping, the spindle length changes and sends a series of impulses to the spinal cord which leads to a reflex and subsequent contraction of the muscle. This is what happens when one tries to touch one's toes very fast. It is basically a protective mechanism to prevent mechanical damage caused by the muscle stretching too far.

It has been proposed that the reactivity of the muscle spindles can be increased by plyometrics. The neuromuscular system is trained to react to the stretch by contracting "hard and fast". The good news is that the stretch does not have to be to the maximum for the muscle spindles to react, but it does need to be fast. The energy which is primed at the site of "explosion" will be lost if the stretch is too slow.

This type of training is particularly appropriate to Rugby League, which is a power game. In terms of sprinting, it is the ability to accelerate that is more important in many respects than maximum speed. So also in Rugby League, it is the ability to make a break over a short distance that often determines the result of the match. Also important is "collision power", which is the ability to collide with great intensity and then move forward in the collision. All else being equal, the more powerful player will be the better player as he will be able to perform more work in the same amount of time, or the same work in less time.

Plyometrics Drills

When executed in the correct manner, plyometrics drills are very intense and have an extreme effect on the muscular system. It is therefore imperative that, in a systematic form, intensive plyometric training is never undertaken by children under 16; with any athletes, it should only be undertaken after one year of lower-body strength training. The primary reason for this is that plyometrics place a lot of stress on muscles during the eccentric or lengthening phase. The legs need to be prepared for this with weight training.

A set of plyometric drills may last approximately four to 12 seconds, and there should be 30–60 seconds rest in between. Each exercise is often repeated three or four times. A session should generally last 15–30 minutes.

Squat Jump

1.   Stand in an upright position, with feet a shoulder width apart. Interlock fingers and place hands behind the head.

2.   Start the movement by bending the knees, lowering yourself to a half-squat position.

3.   Then jump explosively and vertically to maximum height.

4.   Upon landing, immediately return to the half-squat position and, without pause, repeat.

Tuck Jump

1.   Assume a comfortable upright stance, with feet a shoulder width apart.

2.   Start the movement by bending the knees.

3.   Immediately explode upwards, using a double arm action and pulling the knees into the chest.

4.   The time spent in contact with the ground should be as short as possible.

Single-leg Hopping

1. On one leg hop forwards, minimising your time in contact with the ground.

2. A fast leg thrust and vigorous arm movement is required.

3. Try to emphasise speed with every hop. Then repeat this drill using the opposite leg.

Cycled Split Squats

1. Assume a "lunge" position, with one leg extended forward and the other behind the midline of the body. The forward leg should be slightly flexed.

2. Start with a slight counter-movement, then explosively jump off the front leg using the calves of the back leg and thigh muscles of the front leg and quickly switch the legs from front to back while in mid-air.

3. When landing there should be minor leg flexion, and the jump should be repeated immediately

Bounding

1. Start with one foot slightly ahead of the other, as if beginning a stepforward, with arms at the sides. You may walk or jog into the position.

2. Push off with the front leg and drive the back knee up and out. Try to "hang" in the air to increase the distance covered.

3. Prepare the legs and arms for contact with the surface and execution of the next bound. Repeat with the opposite leg immediately upon landing.

4. Each stride should be as powerful as possible.

Hop/Stride

1. Start with one leg slightly in front of the other. Flex the front leg, and explosively hop forwards.

2. On landing, bend the same leg to absorb contact, before again explosively pushing off with the same foot. This time bring the rear leg forward so that it contacts the floor on landing.

3. Push off with this foot and hop forward. Repeat this sequence of movement.

Side-step

1. Running forward, step alternately to the left and right with a slight knee bend.

2. Aim to drive as "wide" and as fast as possible.

Cone Jumps

SIDE

1. Stand to the left side of the cone and jump sideways over the cone to land immediately at the right side.

2. On landing, bend slightly at the knees. Repeat the action as quickly as possible in the opposite direction.

DIAGONAL

1. The cones are placed in a line approximately 0.5–0.75m apart. Start by standing in between and to the left side of two cones.

2. Jump at 45° over the cone in front of you and, upon landing, repeat in the opposite direction as quickly as possible.

FRONT

1. The cones are placed approximately one metre apart. Jump over the cones in a forward direction.

Bunny Jumps

1. From an upright stance, bend at the knees to the half-squat position with the shoulders forward and the arms back.

2.   From here jump outward and upward as far as possible by forcibly extending the hips and knees.

3.   Upon landing, try not to bend further than the half-squat position and repeat immediately.

Jump and Jump

1.   From an upright stance bend at the knees to the half-squat position and then jump to the side as far as possible.

2.   Upon landing, react and jump forward as far as possible. Repeat in the opposite direction.

Double Hamstring Flick

1.   From an upright standing position, jump in the air and flex both legs at the knee so that the ankles touch the buttocks.

2.   Return the feet to the floor as fast as possible and repeat the movement.

3.   Fast lower-limb movement is essential, with minimal movement of the upper body.

Ankle Hops

1.   From an upright standing position, bend by approximately 10cm at the knee, and then quickly reverse the motion and jump into the air, with the drive coming from an extension of the ankles.

2.   Upon landing, flex immediately and repeat the action as quickly as possible.

Slalom

1.   The principle is similar to that of the side-step, but the exercise is performed with both feet together.

2.   Attempt to drive "wide" and fast, with a moderate flexion of the knees.

Plyometrics – Box Drills

Alternate Push-off

1. Start in front of a box 12 to 24ins high with the right foot on the box and the other on the floor.

2. Drive off the right foot as high as possible.

3. Change legs in mid-air so that the left foot lands on the box.

4. Speed is essential, and there should be minimal time spent in contact with the box.

Stride Jump Crossover

1. Start at the side of the box, with the right foot on it and the left just to the side.

2. The aim is to jump from side to side, so the leg on the box drives high and the other pushes to the left.

3. Land with the left foot on the box and the right just to the side of the box.

4. Maximum height and minimum contact time are essential. Use the arms to assist.

5. Repeat the movement as quickly as possible.

Jumps Up (Heavy players)

1. Stand in front of the box.

2. Flex at the knees and jump as high as possible into the air, landing on the box.

3. From here, step off and repeat.

Side-to-Side Jumps (Light and well-conditioned players)

1. Stand to the left side of the box.

2. Flex at the knees and jump sideways on to the box.

3. Immediately jump off the box to land at the right side.

4. Repeat this movement straight away to land at the left side of the box.

5. Speed is essential, and there should be minimal time spent on the box.

Ballistic Push-ups

1. In the normal push-up position, lower yourself by flexing at the elbow.

2. Upon reaching the deep position, with chest close to the floor, push up explosively and, from a 45° angle, continue the movement into the air.

3. Upon landing, repeat the movement.

4. A variation is that, during stage 2 above, as the hands come off the floor into the air, clap them before landing.

5. A further variation sees a medicine ball positioned on the floor beneath the upper chest/chin. As the hands explode upwards from the floor, aim to land them on top of the medicine ball. Then push off the medicine ball into the air, to land with the hands on the floor again.

Plyometrics – Medicine ball

Chest Press

1. Stand in an upright position, with the arms slightly flexed and out horizontally in front of the body and palms facing forwards.

2. A partner throws a medicine ball towards your chest.

3. Try to catch the medicine ball while minimising flexion of the arms on receiving it.

4. Immediately throw back the medicine ball, explosively to your partner, with power coming particularly from the wrist and fingers.

Military Press Throw

1. Stand upright, holding a medicine ball directly above the head with the arms fully extended.

2. While looking upwards towards the medicine ball, bend the arms and throw the ball directly upwards in a straight line.

3. On catching the medicine ball again, try to minimise flexion of the arms and throw the ball back into the air immediately through a rapid extension of the arms and shoulders.

Leg Press

1. Lie on your back, bring your knees into your chest, and raise your pelvis off the ground.

2. A partner throws a medicine ball at your feet, whereupon you should extend the legs and forcefully propel the medicine ball forwards with the soles of the feet.

Power Drop and Return

1. Lie on your back, with arms held vertically upwards but slightly flexed and palms also facing upwards.

2. A partner stands over your head facing your feet and drops a medicine ball towards your hands and chest.

3. Catch the medicine ball, trying to minimise arm flexion, and propel the ball vertically upwards as quickly and explosively as possible.

Hamstring Flick

1. Stand in an upright position with a medicine ball held on the ground between the ankles.

2. Explosively flex the legs and flick the ball vertically upwards behind you. Turn and catch the ball.

Side Pass

1. Stand in pairs approximately three to five metres apart.

2. Player 1 faces straight ahead, holding the ball close to the right side of his chest.

3. He thrusts the ball to his partner as vigorously as possible, who then returns the ball immediately.

4. After throwing, maintain the arms in a slightly flexed position.

Trunk Rotation

1. Stand in pairs back to back.

2. Player 1, with the medicine ball, twists at the trunk to the left to give the ball to Player 2, who has twisted to his right.

3. Continue in this manner. The exercise can also be done individually, as shown in the photographs.

Pullover Pass

1. Player 1 lies on his back, with knees bent and feet flat on the floor, and a medicine ball held at floor level above his head.

2. Player 2 stands at Player 1's feet, facing him.

3. With straight arms, Player 1 throws the ball vigorously to his partner.

CHAPTER 6

ENDURANCE (AEROBIC AND ANAEROBIC)

General aerobic conditioning is normally done by the player away from the club, and provides the base for later high-intensity interval and speed work. The amount of this training required will depend upon the aerobic fitness of the player. The player needs to work at such an intensity that his heartbeat is approximately 75 per cent of its maximum (which maximum is 220 minus one's age) for a duration of at least 20 minutes three times per week. This intensity defines the player's "training zone". So, a player aged 20 should attain a heartbeat of 150 per minute, and one of 30 a rate of 140 beats per minute. A simple way of progressing is to increase the distances which are run, while other forms of aerobic training include cycling and swimming. Lots of slow aerobic training should not be done during the season, however, as it has a negative effect on muscle girth and power performance.

Aerobic training improves the efficiency of the heart and lungs, and also toughens tendons, ligaments and connective tissues.

One form of aerobic training is to do a series of shorter runs interspersed by short low-intensity rest periods, e.g., six 1,000-metre runs with 30-second jog recovery periods. The principle remains that the heart rate must stay within the training zone during both work and rest periods.

Such training can increase the intensity of the work that can be performed by the player's aerobic system. Other forms of aerobic exercise are "fartlek" training or interval training, where the work periods are between two and eight minutes with equal rest periods. Fartlek training involves jogging, normally on an undulating surface, alternated with periods of fast running or hill work. It is a good transition for the player in preparation for the more intense interval training which is required to train his anaerobic system.

Interval training also involves a number of work periods interspersed with periods of rest. The rest periods depend upon the level of fitness of the player, the time in the training year, and the object of the session. They should involve some light exercise, e.g., walking and stretching, rather than allowing the player to collapse on the ground.

The concept of interval training was developed over 50 years ago, but the general guidelines still apply. These are that the athletes should work with a heart rate of over 180 beats per minute, but that their heart rate should have dropped to 120 at the end of the rest period.

The player can progress in interval training by increasing the number of intervals, shortening the rest periods, or increasing the speed of the runs. The coach must be aware of the different effects of the progressions. To increase the number of repetitions or to reduce the rest period will mean that the player will be performing each set at a lower intensity. Higher intensity can be achieved via fewer repetitions, greater rest periods, but more difficult target times. The work/rest intervals are as follows:

Work time	Approximate distance	Rest/time ratio
Over 3 mins.	<1,000m	1:1/1:3
1 - 3 mins.	400m+	1:3/1:4
10 sec - 1 min.	80m+	1:3/1:5
Less than 10 sec	Up to 80m	1:5/1:8

The coach should not underestimate the rest time. If the player does not get the required rest he will not perform at the correct intensity, and therefore the metabolic systems will be stressed differently than was intended. The number of interval sessions could be up to four per week in the off-season depending upon other training commitments, but one or two would be more normal. The game itself is a heavy interval session, and it would not be normal to have more than one strenuous interval session per week during training in season. The total distance covered during that session will vary, but will be in the range of 1,500 to 5,000m.

Particular interval sessions may be used in different ways; let us take 9 x 200m as an example. Let us say that the player has a personal best of 30 seconds for the 200 metres: this is 100 per cent intensity. If the session was designed to emphasise lactic acid tolerance and working with insufficient rest, he may do each of his 200-metre runs in a target time of 36 seconds with only 108-second rest periods (i.e., a ratio of 1:3). If the session was geared more to quality and maintaining high speed, the coach may wish to split the intervals into three sets, e.g., three runs each at under 32 seconds with 160 seconds between them (a ratio of 1:5) and a five-minute jog between sets. Once the basic principles are understood, the coach should be able to match the needs of his players at all times of the year.

Many game-related sessions can be devised using balls, bags, shields or patterns run in the game. Interval work, particularly in-season, should not be solely limited to "track" sessions. The length of time spent on the drill and the work/rest ratio can be altered according to which energy system you most want to stress. Training must be made specific, otherwise the team will consist of well-conditioned athletes but not ones who are conditioned to play Rugby League.

The Great Britain Academy Squad involved in game specific conditioning whilst in camp at Lilleshall.

CHAPTER 7

FLEXIBILITY

Flexibility is not only an important component of physical fitness, but also beneficial for future health. An increase in flexibility can help reduce soft-tissue injuries by allowing greater freedom of movement before training occurs. Increases in the flexibility of the hip and leg muscles can provide an increased stride length and also improve the efficiency of running. It is important that a stretching programme accompanies any strength programme, as the latter on its own can cause muscle shortening.

Increases in flexibility are attained through a programme of stretching. Stretching should take place before and after all training sessions, and matches. Warm muscles are more easily stretched, therefore stretching should take place after a good warm-up. The general warm-up might involve non-specific work such as jogging on the spot or the exercise bike, while a more specific warm-up may involve simple ball skill drills carried out at a steadily increasing pace. The player should not be running beyond 75 per cent pace or twisting and turning sharply at this stage. The warm-up should merely elevate the heart rate and body temperature, i.e., make the player slightly out of breath. Do not forget to warm up the upper body prior to any match, weight training session, or contact drill. Prior to the match, a warm-up period can also help the player to focus his mind. Once the general warm-up is complete, stretching may then take place.

There are different types of stretching which can be classified in a number of different ways. Primarily, stretches can be either passive or active. Active stretches involve the athlete contracting one muscle in order to stretch another, and can be static, dynamic or ballistic. Passive stretching has the athlete relaxed, with a partner or a device such as a towel or band stretching the muscle. A special method of passive stretching is known as PNF (Proprio-Neuromuscular Facilitation), and this also involves the action of a training partner.

Active Static Stretching

Active static stretching is the simplest and safest to carry out. It involves the athlete slowly stretching into a given position and then holding the stretch for a length of time. The length of time varies from five seconds to a minute, although 30 seconds is about the norm. The player carries out the stretch three times, each time trying to extend the range of motion. This should be done gently and not forced.

Active Dynamic Stretching

Dynamic stretching involves sports-specific movements and is common among track athletes, e.g., high knee running prior to sprinting or hurdling.

Active Ballistic Stretching

Ballistic stretching involves bouncing at the end of the stretch position and is not to be recommended as it can cause muscle scarring.

Passive Static Stretching

PNF (Proprio-Neuromuscular Facilitation) involves the use of a partner. There are three types of this stretch, the simplest of which involves an isometric contraction by the player against the hold of his partner. This type of stretching takes time to be taught safely and efficiently and, as there is little evidence of its superiority over active static stretching, the latter is to be recommended.

The Stretches

When doing lower-body stretches make sure that the knee is in line with the toe, and when doing upper-body stretches, try to relax the lower body. Always move slowly into the stretch and gently increase the intensity; the stretch should not hurt. Never bounce in the stretch.

The Calf

1. Leaning against a wall or partner, the player should place his legs one in front of the other as if in a standing start position. He then bends the front knee forward, but keeps his back foot glued to the ground.

2. In a squat position, the player bends his ankles forward while trying to keep his thighs parallel to the floor.

The Front Thigh

1. Standing upright on one leg, the player takes hold of the other shin so that it comes up tight to the buttocks. Different parts of the muscle will be stressed depending upon the degrees of hip and knee flexion. The player should not allow the knee to drift to one side, and should keep the abdominals taut.

2. Lying on his side, the player holds the other shin and pulls it back to the buttocks, in a similar way to No. 1.

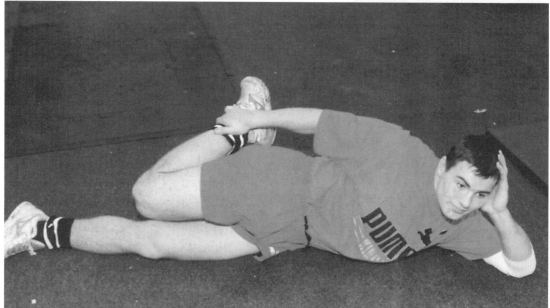

The Rear Thigh

1. The player sits down with his legs straddled, keeping his back straight, and reaches forward from the waist as far as he can.

2. Lying on his back, the player lifts one leg vertically and grasps it by the upper calf. The other leg should be bent, with the foot flat on the floor. He then, slowly pulls the slightly bent leg towards his face.

3.   Crouching with one foot slightly in front of the other, the player bends his rear leg and using both hands rests his body on this leg. Keeping the front leg slightly bent, he slowly points his toes upwards towards his shin. This will also stretch the calf.

The Inner Thigh

1. The player sits with his knees bent and thrust outwards, and the soles of his feet together. Holding his ankles, he then leans forward from the hips. A variation is to keep the back upright and to push the knees down.

2. Sitting with his knees straight and his legs as wide apart as possible, the player rotates from the waist and leans forward from the hips over one leg at a time.

3. Squatting down with feet facing outwards, the player places his elbows on the inside of the thighs and slowly pushes his legs apart.

Hip Flexors and Hip Joints

1. Standing with one leg out behind him and bending the other knee in front of him, the player should try to "push" his rear hip forward.

2. Lying on his back on a bench, the player pulls each knee up to his chest in turn.

Lower Back

1. The player sits with his left leg extended and his right leg bent with the foot outside the left knee. The player turns his upper body, while remaining in an upright position, so that the left elbow is placed outside

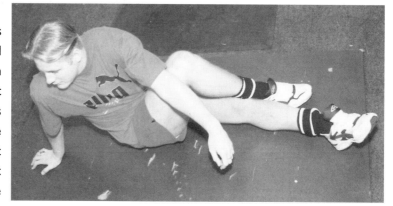

the right thigh. The right hand is kept flat on the floor behind the body, while the chin points in the same direction as the right shoulder.

Abdominals

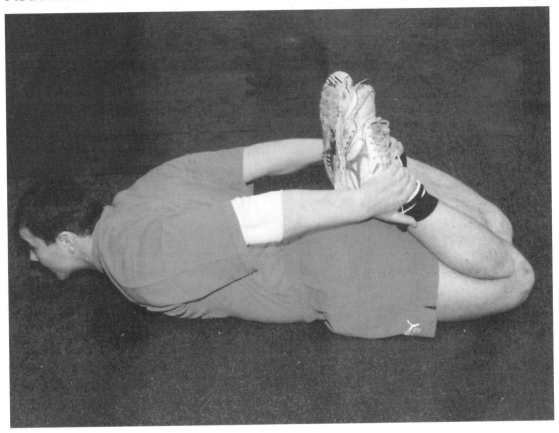

1. Lying on his stomach the player presses his upper body up off the ground by arching his back.

2. Lying on his stomach the player grabs his ankles and lifts his knees and shoulders off the ground.

Upper Back

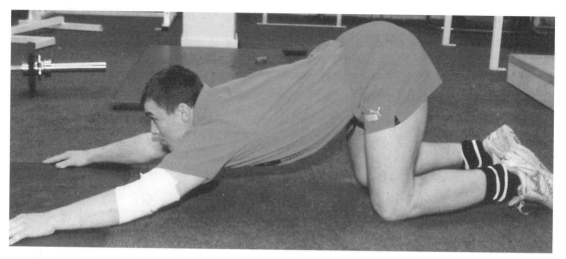

1.   Holding on to a post, the player squats down, leaning back on his arms.

2.   Kneeling on all fours, the player extends his arms forward and lowers his chest to the floor. He then exhales and presses down on his arms to arch his back.

Chest, Shoulders and Upper Arms

1.   Holding a stick or towel above his head with straight arms, the player tries to lower it behind his neck.

2.   Linking his hands behind his back, and with straight arms, the player tries to raise them without bending at the waist.

3.   Standing with his fingers interlocked together, palms upwards and elbows straight, the player tries to reach for the sky behind his head. His elbows should be behind his ears.

4.   Grasping one elbow with the opposite hand, the player tries to press it down behind his head.

5.   Grasping one upper arm with the opposite hand, the player pulls that arm across the front of his body parallel to the ground.

Neck

The player should perform a four-way isometric contraction using his hand as resistance. He should do this while seated and retaining good posture.

There are also stretches for the muscles of the forearms, fingers and feet, but these will normally only be needed during specific rehabilitation. Stretches have a very important role in injury prevention and rehabilitation.

CHAPTER 8

NUTRITION

Many rugby players train like heroes and eat like fools. They spend hours refining their skills and developing their strength and speed, yet do not pay sufficient attention to the food they eat. Training and playing are very demanding on the body's energy resources, and not eating correctly will lead to their depletion and a consequent reduction in performance. Another major area of concern for the player should be fluid intake.

The essential components of diet include water, minerals, vitamins, and the three food types – carbohydrates, fats and proteins. When we eat normally we take in all of these elements; the important thing is to manage their respective quantities.

Water

The human body is made up largely of water. The proportion of water in the fluids of the body is extremely important, so important that disruption may have life-threatening consequences. Water is taken in by drinking and by eating foods, particularly fruit and vegetables, which have a high water content. Water is used by the body in a number of ways, for instance, the breakdown of large food molecules, or detoxification of the products of protein metabolism. But by far the most obvious water loss associated with exercise is through sweating.

During the metabolic processes which convert food into the energy required for muscular work, a lot of heat energy is produced as a by-product. When the body is working hard, more heat is produced than is required to maintain a steady body temperature. If this heat is not lost from the body, the person will overheat and ultimately die. One of the ways the body has of overcoming this is to sweat; the evaporation of the sweat from the skin cools the body. When exercising strenuously in a warm environment, an athlete can lose two litres of sweat per hour; an 80kg player who trains for two hours may therefore shed 5 per cent of his body weight. Serious impairment of performance can occur with as little as 2 per cent loss in total body water, while a 5 per cent loss can reduce work capacity by 30 per cent. As the fluid volume of the blood decreases, the ability of the circulatory system to deliver food and oxygen and remove waste products from the muscles is reduced.

In their general diet, players should make sure that they have sufficient water, fruit juice, low-fat milk, and fresh fruit and vegetables. A simple test is to look at one's urine: if it is coloured, then one is dehydrated to some extent. Caffeine encourages water loss from the body, and so players should not depend solely on tea and coffee for fluid replacement.

It is a good idea for the player to weigh himself before and after training (although not in his training kit!) As a rough guide, a weight loss of 1kg means that one litre of fluid needs to be replaced.

It is particularly vital that players have adequate fluid supply before, during and after exercise. Prior to exercise, they should take in up to half a litre within half an hour of training or playing. Fluid should then be taken at regular intervals throughout the exercise period. Many food supplement companies advertise a whole range of fluid replacement drinks but, unless money is of no object, water will suffice. The loss of salts when we sweat is minimal compared with the loss of water and, so long as the player has adequate supplies of these within his diet, there should be no drop in performance. Long-duration endurance athletes such as marathon runners may benefit from the intake of carbohydrate drinks, but coaches should be wary of administering them to rugby players as they may slow down the uptake of fluid by the body.

Carbohydrates

This group of compounds is the body's major energy source. Carbohydrate is stored in the form of glycogen in the muscles and liver. Under the control of body chemicals called hormones, the glycogen is released to provide the energy for the body. The stores of glycogen cannot be maintained without regular and adequate carbohydrate intake. Most activities involved in playing and training for Rugby League involve the utilisation of carbohydrate. The more often and more intensely a player trains the more he will deplete his glycogen stores. It may take as long as two days to replenish completely the glycogen lost during intense exercise such as weight training or a match. Players should aim to get at least half of their energy requirements from carbohydrates.

Muscle glycogen levels

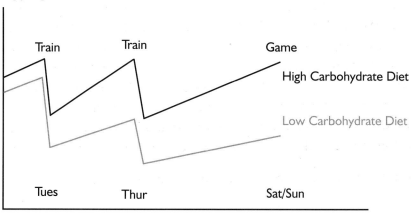

The graph on the previous page shows the effects of heavy training associated with inadequate carbohydrate intake. By the time match-day comes, the player on the poor diet has insufficient fuel for a complete performance.

Carbohydrates consist of starchy foods such as bread, potatoes, pasta, grains and beans, and simple sugars. These starchy "complex carbohydrates" provide the body with a steady, slow release of energy. They also provide minerals, vitamins, fibre and, in the case of beans and grains, protein.

Complex carbohydrates should be the mainstay of a player's diet, but simple carbohydrates are also a useful source of readily available energy. Fruits, sweets, soft drinks and energy bars are easily digested and comprise an excellent snack. Spreads such as jam and golden syrup are an easy way of adding extra carbohydrates to your diet.

The rugby player should therefore take the following practical steps to avoid carbohydrate depletion:

1. Make bread, rice, pasta and potatoes the main items of your meals.

2. Eat fruit as dessert and as snacks.

3. Eat a large quantity of breakfast cereals – they are an excellent late-night snack.

4. Gradually increase your carbohydrate intake two days before the game, taking smaller, more frequent meals which are easier to digest.

5. Get into the habit of eating food containing simple sugars immediately after training/playing, e.g., fruit, biscuits, boiled sweets, sports drinks.

6. In the first few hours after training/playing place the emphasis on eating simple sugars, as these replace glycogen more adequately than complex carbohydrates.

Protein

This is the food type used in growth and repair. The most "usable" sources of protein are found in animal foodstuffs, particularly egg whites. But complete proteins can be obtained from vegetable sources, provided that a mixture of sources is used – the main requirement being to mix cereals and beans. Vegetable protein sources have the disadvantage in not being utilised so efficiently by the body. However, they are normally found in foods rich in fibre and carbohydrates, whereas animal protein is often associated with a high degree of fat.

There is debate over the amount of protein needed by athletes, particularly those engaged in heavy weights programmes, as compared to the sedentary individual. If more protein is required it should be taken in small, low-fat quantities such as half a litre of low-fat milk, or 20 grammes of water-packed tuna. The use of protein supplements is normally unnecessary and can be a distinct hindrance to athletic performance by increasing the amount of water required to deal with the by-products of protein metabolism, and reducing valuable carbohydrate intake by repressing appetite. If a player is on a weight-gain programme and has upped his protein intake, he should make sure that the gains in weight are lean muscle mass and not just gains in fat!

Fats

Fat consumption in developed countries is too high. Eating fat is the easiest way of becoming fat. Fat contains certain essential vitamins, but these are easily obtained in a balanced diet and can be stored in the body for several months. Fat interferes with muscle contraction and is only used as a fuel during low-intensity endurance work. Excess fat is of no use to the Rugby League player.

Minerals and Vitamins

If the player is following a sensible diet he should not need supplementation in this area. However, a simple vitamin and mineral tablet can sometimes be used as an insurance.

Practical Implications

1. Increase your intake of starchy food. Try to eat complex carbohydrates at every meal. In the days approaching a match, increase this further.

2. Make sure that you have an adequate supply of fluid. Take a litre of water to training and sip this regularly throughout. Know how much fluid you need to replace.

3. Eat some carbohydrate immediately after training or playing; bananas are an excellent source of readily available carbohydrate and of potassium. Make sure that you have eaten well during the day prior to training, and eat a high carbohydrate meal within two hours of intense training.

4. Reduce the total fat intake, particularly of animal fat.

5. On match-day, do not eat food rich in protein or fat. Do not eat within two hours of playing. Make sure that you have adequate fluid intake.

6. If you wish to gain weight, eat five or six smaller meals throughout the day.

7.   If you wish to lose weight, reduce your fat and alcohol intakes, while increasing your intake of fruit and vegetables, and step up your aerobic conditioning.

Post-match Eating/Drinking

Players should try to replace their glycogen sources as soon as possible after either playing or training. Within 20 minutes a player should consume 100 grammes of simple carbohydrates, which is approximately equivalent to four bananas or half a litre of sports' drink. Simple sugars are absorbed more quickly into the body. After training or playing the body becomes tuned to store food; thus, within two hours, the player should consume a meal rich in both simple and complex carbohydrates. If he is not hungry, a high-carbohydrate replacement drink could be used.

Players should also make sure that they are adequately rehydrated. They should not drink alcohol until they have had a colourless urination.

CHAPTER 9

QUESTION AND ANSWER

1. Why is it necessary to warm up, and what is a cool-down?

Every training session should begin with a warm-up, which is a period of low-intensity activity which prepares the body for more strenuous aspects of the session. It should consist of gentle jogging, skills drills, or small-sided games. It has been shown that a five-minute warm-up can elevate muscle temperature for up to 45 minutes. This is important as it allows muscles to stretch more effectively, so increasing the range of movement around a joint. The warm-up also directs more blood to these muscles which will be used in the session, so that they can work harder and for longer. It increases the activity of certain enzymes, thereby allowing muscles to contract faster. A total body warm-up therefore reduces the risk of injury and prepares the player both physically and mentally for physical exertion. It should cause light to mild sweating, and leave the player slightly out of breath.

A cool-down should take place after every session. It should comprise low-intensity jogging for one to two minutes, with two to three minutes' stretching. This helps to rid the body of waste products which may have built up during the session, by sending oxygenated blood to the muscles. It also gradually reduces the heart rate so that blood does not pool, but is pumped back to the heart.

2. What is the best way to lose fat?

This is a very popular question, and a multi-million-pound industry has grown up around this subject. The average adult may contain 30–70 billion fat cells. Unfortunately, it is impossible to reduce the number of fat cells, as it seems that the number is set down during childhood and other periods of growth, along with their distribution over the body. Males who have excess fat around the abdominal region are likely always to have a significant amount of fat there. However, the good news is that, with a consistent effort, it is possible to empty the cells and so make the person look less fat. Despite previous claims, it is not possible to do this by "sweating it out" or "spot reduction", which means trying to lose fat from specific areas by doing things like sit-ups. The way to lose fat is to reduce your calorific intake and increase your calorific expenditure. Fat is an excellent form of energy and needs to be metabolised by your working muscles, i.e., burned away into the atmosphere.

This requires continuous exercise using large muscle groups, such as jogging, cycling, swimming or aerobics, where the person elevates the heart rate to around 140 beats per minute for 20–30 minutes two or three times a week. This low-intensity, "conversational" exercise takes fat to the working muscles from all over the body, so that a general reduction of fat is achieved rather than a specific reduction. One pound of fat equals 3,500 calories, and could be lost during a week by a combination of healthy eating and exercise. For example, four runs of 30–40 minutes a week would burn approximately 1,200 calories and a lower food intake of 300 calories a day could quite easily be achieved.

3. What is cross-training, and is it necessary for Rugby League players?

One of the most important principles of training is specificity. This means that improvements in physical condition are only observed in the parts of the body which are being exercised or overloaded. It means that arm exercises will not increase leg strength, and bench press will not improve your ability to do arm curls. It has also been proved that changes within muscles are specific to the range of motion that you are working in. Similarly, doing arm curls to improve pure strength will not necessarily make a great difference to the muscular endurance of your biceps. Therefore the improvements in running after an eight-week cycling programme will be minor compared to those at the end of an eight-week running programme. This needs to be borne in mind when training.

However, a new form of exercise has become popular which is known as cross-training. This involves mixing up the training programme with different types of exercise. While excellent for the casual exerciser, this should be done primarily in the off-season for Rugby League players. For a period of maybe two or three weeks, depending on the level at which one plays, it will add variety to rugby training and improve general fitness.

Thus the player may engage in a combination of jogging, cycling, swimming, rowing, aerobics, squash, basketball, badminton, touch rugby, etc. These activities should become less evident when specific preparation begins, but still have a role to play in the form of recovery exercise. On the day after a match, or when recovering from injury, the player may take part in any of the above activities. Cycling and swimming are excellent forms of cardiovascular exercise, but should never take precedence over running as this is what happens in a Rugby League match.

4. Will speed drills make me faster in a game?

The principle behind the speed drill is to make the runner more efficient at moving through space, or to make him more streamlined. If his arms move straight forward and back, he is moving through less space than if his arms move out to the side. If his face is relaxed his shoulders will be relaxed, meaning they can drive back further. It is the same with the legs: if the runner's heel follows through to the buttock then, as the knee lifts, the heel is tucked in. This means there is less resistance on its movement forward, and the leg will therefore travel more quickly.

The greatest exponents of this type of training have been the East Europeans who, to a certain extent, have manufactured many sprinters and have therefore proved that it is possible to run faster by improving your technique. This can be applied to Rugby League. When a player has made a break, is supporting or chasing in defence, he needs to run as quickly as possible, and technique can make a great difference. A relaxed, long stride and good arm drive could enable a defender eventually to ankle-tap a sprinting attacker. However, the attacker with the ball cannot be relaxed as he needs to prepare his body for the collision which is likely to ensue: he is trying to run fast, but must remain tense to withstand that collision. There are actually very few opportunities in a game to run at top speed, as most of the time the attacker is accelerating. Speed drills should thus be an integral part of Rugby League training but need to be placed in context.

5. What is overtraining?

Overtraining has been a problem in sport for many years. It is the result of overstressing the player both physically and mentally, and causes abnormal psychological and physiological performance responses. It tends to occur most of all in highly-motivated players, and does not happen overnight but generally builds up over a period of weeks and months. There are various signs and symptoms, as shown below:

1. Increased resting heart rate;

2. Slow recovery of heart rate after exercise;

3. Decreased appetite and weight loss;

4. Disturbed sleep;

5. Early fatigue during training;

6. Increased susceptibility to infections;

7. Slow healing from cuts;

8. Lack of concentration.

When overtraining has been recognised, the player must be made aware that a wealth of research has been conducted into this subject, and the solution is always rest. Improved diet and more sleep will quickly help the player to return to his normal self.

It is important to note that the authors have never seen a case of overtraining in Rugby League and would be very surprised if they did. It happens most often with distance athletes and swimmers. With a scientifically correct training programme, few Rugby League players will ever succumb to this. With the appropriate intensity, the duration of training need not be excessive and, while players will become highly fatigued, overtraining should not be an issue.

6. How long a rest period do I need between sets when weight training?

This is a subject of much debate among weight trainers. Players are frequently criticised by coaches for spending too much time talking and not enough time training, but the balance depends on what type of training they are doing. If the aim of the session is to develop strength, then rest periods of two-and-a-half to three minutes are essential. This is because each set depletes the most powerful energy system (ATP-PC), which takes two to three minutes to replenish. While the coach may think that the player is ready, he cannot actually work to 100 per cent until his energy stores are replete.

In contrast, when training for muscle growth, the rest periods are reduced to one to two minutes and, in some cases, to 45–60 seconds. This leads to moderately high lactic acid concentrations in the blood, which may be one of the reasons that the muscle grows as these increase the capillary network of the muscle. Such short rest periods also increase the secretion of growth hormone.

If the aim of the session is to improve muscular endurance, then rest periods are cut to less than 30 seconds and, in some cases, to no rest at all. This pushes lactic acid levels very high, causing acidity and thus fatigue. If muscles are trained in this manner then they may develop systems to tolerate this pain so that the player can be stronger for longer.

The coach and the player must therefore be aware of the aim of the session and adhere to the relevant rest period. The long rest periods for strength training can be filled with abdominal work or flexibility work, as long as the subsequent training intensity is very high.

7. What is the bottom line for Rugby League players?

Rugby League football is arguably the most physically demanding team sport in the world. To be a consistently good player you need strength, speed, power, flexibility and various forms of endurance, but the bottom line is power. Speed alone is of no use if there is no strength behind it: strong muscles will allow a player to reach his top speed before an equally fast player with less strength, that is, it will allow him to accelerate more quickly, which is what we are seeking. Above all, muscular power will enable a player both to withstand and to impart a high amount of force against an opponent who is attempting to do the same thing to him.

Players need to spend a great deal of time doing strength and resistance training both in the gym and, more importantly, on the training field. Pure resistance work and resistance endurance will make players stand out more in game situations. If 13 players train in this manner then they will be better prepared than 13 players who prepare with just touch rugby or athletics training.

8. At what age should children start intensive training?

Numerous research projects have been carried out into the effects of exercise and various training programmes on children. There are no clear-cut answers to date, but there are several key messages.

Flexibility

Great emphasis should be placed on flexibility to prevent the loss which occurs as children grow older. The coach should try to introduce the habit of stretching, before and after training and playing.

Aerobic Endurance

It is possible for pre- and post-pubescents to improve their aerobic capacity to the same extent as adults. This should be done with small-sided, Rugby League-related competitive games and skills drills. The coach should encourage children to participate in cross-country at school and, from the age of 14 or 15, introduce one aerobic session a week of 15– 20 minutes at a conversational level.

Anaerobic Endurance

It has been shown that an anaerobic training programme can increase the levels of intramuscular fuel stores in 11–15-year-olds, thus improving this type of endurance. Small-sided, Rugby League-related competitive games and skills drills will again do this, and there is no need for structured anaerobic sessions before the age of 14 or 15.

Speed

Soviet research has shown that the best ages to develop leg speed are between 7 and 11 years old. Young children should therefore be encouraged to play as many chasing games as possible, either with a rugby ball or just in the playground. Casual speed drills of low intensity and low impact can be introduced at the age of 14, these being such as hopping, skipping, etc.

Strength

The introduction of mild resistance training can begin for children as young as 10 years of age, but we would recommend the age of 14. It has been proved that this will increase strength and reduce injury and, contrary to popular belief, will not cause bone damage. There should be no fatigue at the end of the set, and competitions between children should be concerned with technique, not weight. Repetitions should be high: 15 or 20 repeated two or three times. There should be long rests and only three or four exercises, with each repetition lasting two to three seconds.

Summary

Physical fitness can start to receive attention from around 14–15 years of age, but should involve very little fatigue. It is important to note that chronological age and biological age may be two or three years apart with teenage boys. Anybody working with children should be aware of the scientific principles of exercise.

9. Does weight training make you "muscle-bound"?

The belief that weight training will reduce flexibility, i.e., that you become "muscle-bound", has been commonly held among a number of coaches in a variety of sports. However, as early as 1956 scientific studies showed that resistance training does not reduce flexibility and, in fact, more recent studies have shown the opposite to be the case – Olympic weight-lifters have been shown to be second only to gymnasts in their flexibility. Nowadays weight training is an integral and unquestioned part of all sports training regimes.

However, the player must make sure that he trains his muscles through the full range of motion (unless specifically told not to by his physio or conditioner), and that he adequately trains both muscles of an antagonistic group so that a strength imbalance does not arise. He must also be sure to carry out a flexibility programme every day, that is, after a gentle full-body warm-up; between sets or interval runs, and as part of his general cool-down.

10. When we do our interval work, our coach has us all running together, and some of the less fit players struggle to keep up: is this a problem?

Each individual player should run his intervals to specific target times for both work and rest. Sometimes this is impractical to administer, particularly for an overworked, under-resourced amateur coach.

However, the coach must take a couple of points on board. First, if the slower players do not get sufficient rest they will not be able to perform the next run with sufficient intensity; thus the quality of the training will drop off, and they will end up doing a form of low-intensity fartlek. As Rugby

League is a game of short, quick bursts interspersed with periods of rest, the training should reflect this. The second problem is the psychological effect which repeatedly coming last will have on team-mates. It is far better to run players of similar speeds together and to overcome the obvious discrepancies between groups, the coach could give each one a different target distance to do in the same time, e.g., 180, 190 or 200 metres in 30 seconds. This type of approach will enable the coach to administer the work:rest ratio more effectively while having groups of similar pace.

11. We all used to have a can of lager after playing, but our new coach has stopped this. He gives us a cup of tea after the game and a glass of fresh orange after training. Is this better?

Unless the tea is decaffeinated it will cause the same problems as the lager. This is because caffeine and alcohol are diuretics, which means that they cause the body to lose water by urination. After a match or training, the body will almost certainly be dehydrated, so the first priority is to replace fluid supplies. (A simple way of seeing how much fluid you lose is to weigh yourself before and after training: 1kg is 1 litre.) The cheapest way to replace fluid is to drink water. Alcohol and caffeine also interfere with vital vitamin uptake.

Orange juice is a different problem. It can help to replace carbohydrate energy, but pure orange will dehydrate you. This is because the stomach needs to absorb water from the rest of the body to dilute the orange to enable it to be passed on to the small intestine.

The best post-exercise drink is something which satisfies both fluid and carbohydrate replacement. The player should dissolve the appropriate amount of carbohydrate food and drink mix in water, maybe with a small pinch of salt and some flavouring, or use a commercially-available sports drink. He should drink this immediately he enters the dressing-room.

12. This book emphasises the importance of the collision in Rugby League. Why is it so important?

Rugby League is a game of physical collision. The speed at which attackers and defenders get up from these collisions, and the nature of the collisions themselves, can influence the outcome of the game.

The analysis project featured in Chapter 2 scientifically proves the point, and all professional coaches now stress as part of their instruction that, when a player carries the ball into the collision, a fast play-the-ball is required to catch the defenders on the back foot. Conversely, players involved in the collision as tacklers are asked to use techniques which are designed to slow down the play-the-ball, so that the defence is in control of the situation.

Which player wins the battle of the collision is dependent upon the following factors:

Weight

Strength

Speed

Endurance

Commitment

Technique

Weight is largely genetically determined, although it can be altered through correct diet and training habits. Speed and strength are both components of power. Speed can be trained in the appropriate way, while raw strength can be successfully developed in the gym and then, with correct strategies, used to increase power. Endurance of the muscular, aerobic and anaerobic types is also essential, so that the collision in minute 80 is as intense as in minute 1.

Commitment is up to the player himself and his hunger for the battle, while technique in the collision, both offensively and defensively, can be mastered through good coaching. It is worth noting at this point that many coaches do man-on-man, or two v one, disciplined tackling practices to perfect the technique as well as using appropriate coaching aids, e.g., hit shields or tackle bags.

In conclusion, a winning team will attribute its success to many factors. Inevitably, one of these is winning the battle of the collision, and this is why it is so important. Therefore the players should physically condition themselves for the collision, monitor their techniques within the collision, and mentally prepare to take part in the collision. If they do this, they will win the battle.

CHAPTER 10

FITNESS TESTING

Before commencing any training programme, it is essential that all players undergo a physical evaluation to make the coach aware of their individual strengths and weaknesses. These can be identified during testing and addressed with an individually specific training programme. Testing is also the best way to monitor players' progress. By repeating appropriate tests at regular intervals the coach can assess the effectiveness of the prescribed training programme. It is also a great way of motivating players, as they are continually attempting to beat their previous scores. Improvement on the tests will boost a player's confidence, which is what most coaches are looking for.

Testing is therefore an effective and consistent method of making players fitter. This does not necessarily mean that they will win more games, but it certainly reduces the chance that they will lose games. If the coach can control the controllable, then the outcome of the match comes down to external factors. Some standards for professional players are outlined below.

The Battery of Tests

1. Body Fat Percentage and Weight

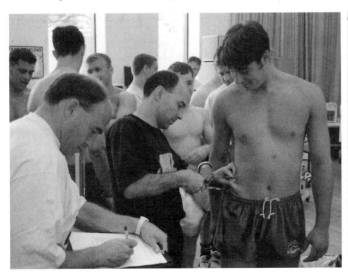 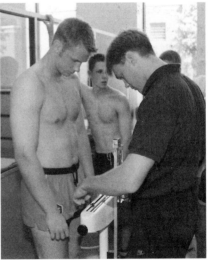

The weight of any individual is the combined weight of a number of different components of the body, including muscle, bone and fat. Fat accumulates in specific sites around the body, and increases if more energy is taken in (i.e., eaten) than is expended. All individuals are expected to have a certain minimum amount of body fat. Measuring an individual's body fat percentage is one of the best ways of assessing whether or not a person is overweight. This is particularly true with sportsmen and women, who may appear to be overweight when using traditional "height/weight" tables, since they often have large amounts of muscle which will make them seem heavy for their height.

First it is necessary to weigh the players, and then to determine each player's body fat percentage by taking four measurements from specific skinfold sites. The four sites used are the biceps, triceps, sub-scapular and supra-iliac areas. In order to obtain useful readings, the same calliper should always be used, and the same person should take the measurements. Any comparison between individuals should be tentative. The four measurements should be added together, and the following table used to convert that total to a percentage.

Table I

Table to convert the sum of four skinfold measurements to an estimated fat content as a percentage measurement of body weight								
MALES (age in years)				FEMALES (age in years)				
Skinfolds	17-29	30-39	40-49	50+	17-29	30-39	40-49	50+
(mm)								
15	4.8	-	-	-	10.5	-	-	-
20	8.1	12.2	12.2	12.6	14.1	17	19.8	21.4
25	10.5	14.2	15	15.6	16.8	19.4	22.2	24
30	12.9	16.2	17.7	18.6	19.5	21.8	24.5	26.6
35	14.7	17.7	19.6	20.8	21.5	23.7	26.4	28.5
40	16.4	19.2	21.4	22.9	23.4	25.5	28.2	30.3
45	17.7	20.4	23	24.7	25	26.9	29.6	31.9
50	19	21.5	24.6	26.5	26.5	28.2	31	33.4
55	20.1	22.5	25.9	27.9	27.8	29.4	32.1	34.6
60	21.2	23.5	27.1	29.2	29.1	30.6	33.2	35.7
65	22.2	24.3	28.2	30.4	30.2	31.6	34.1	36.7
70	23.1	25.1	29.3	31.6	31.2	32.5	35	37.7
75	24	25.9	30.3	32.7	32.2	33.4	35.9	38.7
80	24.8	26.6	31.2	33.8	33.1	34.3	36.7	39.6

85	25.5	27.2	32.1	34.8	34	35.1	37.5	40.4
90	26.2	27.8	33	35.8	34.8	35.8	38.3	41.2
95	26.9	28.4	33.7	36.6	35.6	36.5	39	41.9
100	27.6	29	34.4	37.4	36.4	37.2	39.7	42.6
105	28.2	29.6	35.1	38.2	37.1	37.9	40.4	43.3
110	28.8	30.1	35.8	39	37.8	38.6	41	43.9
115	29.4	30.6	36.4	39.7	38.4	39.1	41.5	44.5
120	30	31.1	37	40.4	39	39.6	42	45.1
125	30.5	31.5	37.6	41.1	39.6	40.1	42.5	45.7
130	31	31.9	38.2	41.8	40.2	40.6	43	46.2
135	31.5	32.3	38.7	42.4	40.8	41.1	43.5	46.7
140	32	32.7	39.2	43	41.3	41.6	44	47.2
145	32.5	33.1	39.7	43.6	41.8	42.1	44.5	47.7
150	32.9	33.5	40.2	44.1	42.3	42.6	45	48.2
155	33.3	33.9	40.7	44.6	42.8	43.1	45.4	48.7
160	33.7	34.3	41.2	45.1	43.3	43.6	45.8	49.2
165	34.1	34.6	41.6	45.6	43.7	44	46.2	49.6
170	34.5	34.8	42	46.1	44.1	44.4	46.6	50
175	34.9	-	-	-	-	44.8	47	50.4
180	35.3	-	-	-	-	45.2	47.4	50.8
185	35.6	-	-	-	-	45.6	47.8	51.2
190	35.9	-	-	-	-	45.9	48.2	51.6
195	-	-	-	-	-	46.2	48.5	52
200	-	-	-	-	-	46.5	48.8	52.4
205	-	-	-	-	-	-	49.1	52.7
210	-	-	-	-	-	-	49.4	53

Table taken from Durnin and Womersley (1974)

The body fat percentage for children is taken from measurement of just two skinfold sites, the triceps and sub-scapular. Adding together the readings from these two skinfolds, the coach should use the table below to ascertain percentages.

Table 2

Table to convert the sum of two skinfold measurements (from children) to an estimated fat content expressed as a percentage of body weight				
Sum of two skinfolds	BOYS		GIRLS	
(mm)	Pre-puberty	Mid-puberty	Pre-puberty	Mid-puberty
5	4.2	2.5	3.8	3.8
10	9.6	7.9	9.5	9.5
15	14.7	13	14.7	14.7
20	19.3	17.6	18.9	18.9
25	23.6	21.9	22.6	22.6
30	27.4	25.7	25.7	25.7

Excellent	=	<10%
Good	=	10–14%
Average	=	14.5–18%
Poor	=	>18%

2. "Sit and Reach" Flexibility Test

This is a simple test designed to give an indication of the flexibility of an individual's hamstrings and lower back. The player must sit on the floor, with his legs out straight and his feet flat against a box.

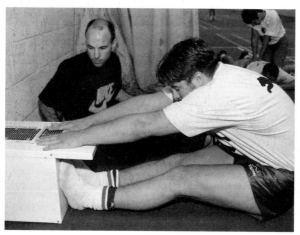

Without bending his knees he must then bend forward with his arms outstretched, and push a sliding scale on the top of the box as far down the box as possible. This is done initially with both legs out straight, and is then repeated with the left and right legs independently of one another, in order to determine whether there are any differences in hamstring flexibility between the two legs. A negative score means that the fingertips do not extend as far as the toes; a score of 0 is level with the toes, and a positive score indicates how far, in centimetres, the player is able to reach beyond his toes. The average score for senior backs and forwards on this test is +14.0cm.

Excellent	=	>18cm
Good	=	12–17.9cm
Average	=	6–11.9cm
Poor	=	<6cm

3. Strength

There are two types of strength testing: the 10RM (repetition maximum) test, and the 1RM test. To complete the 10RM test, the player performs ten consecutive repetitions of the bench press

exercise, has two minutes' rest, increases the weight and repeats, and continues until he can no longer do ten reps. The weight lifted during the last full ten-rep set is his 10RM.

This test is a good indicator of both arm and upper-body strength. Since larger players tend to have an advantage over smaller players in being able to lift weights, the 10RM value for each player can be expressed as a percentage of body weight. Generally, a 10RM value of 100 per cent of body weight is very good, while values of below 80 per cent indicate an urgent need for arm and upper-body strength work.

To complete the 1RM test, the player should follow the same procedure as above, but performing only one repetition instead of ten.

Lower-body strength can be tested using the same format with squats, leg press or the dead lift.

BENCH PRESS 10RM		
Excellent	=	>120%
Good	=	95%–120%
Average	=	75%–95%
Poor	=	<75%

BENCH PRESS 1RM		
Excellent	=	>125kg
Good	=	110–125kg
Average	=	85–110kg
Poor	=	<85kg

DEAD LIFT 1RM		
Excellent	=	>200kg
Good	=	170–200kg
Average	=	135–170kg
Poor	=	<135kg

4. Muscular Endurance

For a player to be strong in the first five minutes is important, but to be strong in the last five minutes may determine the outcome of the game. It is also vital that a player has the capacity to be involved in repetitive collisions over a short period of time. This type of muscular endurance can be tested on a bench press or squat. For upper-body endurance a bench press test is used by many Rugby League clubs, with players pressing an 80lb or 35kg weight as many times as possible at a tempo of one up, one down.

Excellent	=	>80 reps
Good	=	60–79 reps
Average	=	40–60 reps
Poor	=	<40 reps

In order to test the muscular endurance of the abdominal muscles, players must perform as many

sit-ups as they can in time to a series of bleeps emitted by an audio cassette. (The audio cassette for the sit-up test is available from the National Coaching Foundation, 114 Cardigan Road, Leeds, LS6 3BJ. Tel. No. (0113) 274 4802.) The speed at which the sit-ups must be performed is increased at one-minute intervals until the players can no longer maintain the tempo required. The time at which each player drops out is recorded as his performance time on this test. The longer a player continues to exercise, the greater his abdominal endurance. On average, senior players complete four minutes and 25 seconds of work on this test, although many can complete the maximum eight minutes.

Excellent	=	6 min 45 secs – end of tape
Good	=	5 min 15 secs – 6 min 45 secs
Average	=	4 min – 5 min 15 secs
Poor	=	<4 min

5. Power

The ability to exert a high amount of force in a very short space of time is what most coaches and players seek. This can be tested either by simple jumps for height and distance, or in the laboratory. A sergeant jump measurement can be obtained by having the player reach at full stretch up a wall, and marking the point where the tips of his fingers reach. The player then jumps vertically as high as he can and touches the wall and, again, this point is marked. The distance between the two marks

is measured. The greater the distance, the more power generated. A standing horizontal distance jump can also be measured to give an indication of power.

Power is measured in the laboratory using a specially-adapted bicycle ergometer system linked to a microcomputer. Each player is required to perform a series of maximal-effort sprints on the ergometer, while a heavy resistance is applied to the bike which is equivalent to 75 grammes per kilogram of the player's weight. The maximum force produced in accelerating the flywheel against the resistance is recorded by the microcomputer, and related to the player's body weight. This provides a measure of the lower limb power-to-weight ratio for each player.

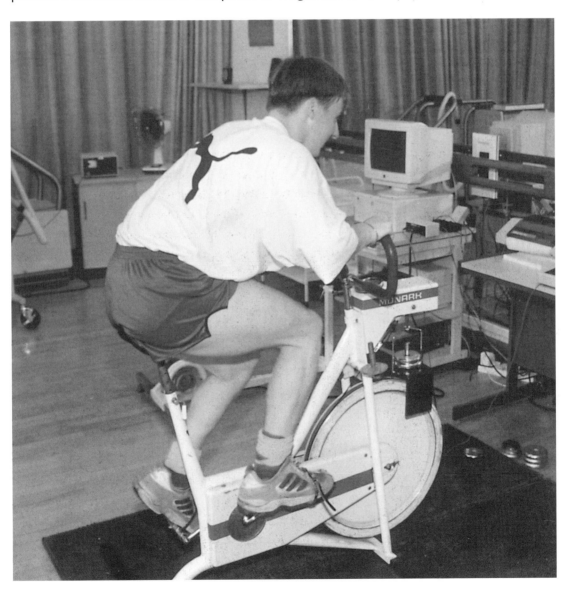

6. Speed

An important fitness requirement is the ability to accelerate quickly from either a stationary or a moving start, and to run at top speed. The most appropriate distances over which to time players are 20 metres and 40 metres. This can be done using a stop watch, although an electronic timing device using a photoelectric cell is accurate to one 100th of a second. The best time for a 20-metre sprint should be used as an indication of the player's ability to accelerate, while leg speed is determined from the 40-metre time.

	20 METRES	40 METRES
Excellent	= <3.00 secs	= <5.25 secs
Good	= 3.10–3.00 secs	= 5.26–5.50 secs
Average	= 3.25–3.11 secs	= 5.51–5.75 secs
Poor	= 3.26 secs	= >5.76 secs

7. Aerobic Endurance

To achieve a high work rate, the player needs to be able to transport a large amount of oxygen from the air to his muscles. The capacity to which he can do this may be assessed by a field test such as the "bleep test" or maximum oxygen uptake test. An individual's maximum oxygen uptake value represents the maximum amount of oxygen which can be supplied to the muscles over a given period of time, and is widely accepted as being the most reliable available indicator of an individual's aerobic fitness. In Rugby League, those players with the highest maximum oxygen uptake values tend

to be the ones who maintain the highest work rates during a match, and who show the least signs of fatigue.

A shuttle run test is used to measure the players' maximum oxygen uptake values. Running up and back between two lines, marked out 20 metres apart in a gymnasium, the players have to keep to a set running speed which is determined by an audio cassette. (The audio cassette is available from the National Coaching Foundation, 114 Cardigan Road, Leeds, LS6 3BJ. Tel. No. (0113) 274 4802.) Each time the cassette bleeps, the players must be at one end of the 20-metre shuttle or the other. After each minute, the time delay between the bleeps decreases, so running speed has to be increased in order to keep up. The players have to run for as long as possible, until they can no longer keep up with the speed set by the tape. The point in the test at which each player drops out is used to predict their maximum oxygen uptake value.

The average score for senior forwards on this test is ten shuttles on Level 12, while the average for backs is four shuttles on Level 13. Those players aspiring to reach the senior ranks should be aiming to achieve at least these scores.

Excellent	=	>6 shuttles/Level 13
Good	=	6 shuttles/Level 12–5 shuttles/Level 13
Average	=	6 shuttles/Level 11–5 shuttles/Level 12
Poor	=	<6 shuttles/Level 11

8. Anaerobic Capacity

As aforementioned, Rugby League involves repeated bursts of high-intensity activity with short rests in between. This causes the build-up of lactic acid which inhibits effective activity, and the ability to prevent or tolerate this accumulation is essential for a top player. The multiple sprint test is designed to assess each player's ability to exercise anaerobically, without experiencing undue fatigue. Each player performs six maximal-effort sprints over a distance of 40 metres, setting off at 30-second intervals, and the time for each sprint is recorded. Fatigue is determined in the following way: the six 40-metre times are added together to give a total time, while the best 40-metre time is multiplied by six to give an optimal time. The drop-off time is the difference between the optimal time and the actual time. Those players who have the smallest drop-off time are those most able to exercise anaerobically.

Excellent	=	<0.9 secs
Good	=	1.5 secs–0.9 sec
Average	=	2.25 secs–1.5 secs
Poor	=	>2.25 secs

Summary

These tests comprise a quite detailed evaluation and will yield valuable data about each player. Ideally, the player should be assessed three times a year, which would allow the coach and sport scientists to structure an appropriate training programme for each individual and to monitor it continually.

CHAPTER 11

DESIGNING TRAINING PROGRAMMES

The construction of a training programme involves the coach in quite a number of decisions which depend upon reasons such as facilities and resources available, the training background of his players, the standard of competition the players will be taking part in, etc. The coach also needs to analyse what his own objectives are in the immediate, medium and long term before devising a structured programme.

The coach must then look at the whole year and break it down into various periods with differing phases. This is a complex procedure and requires sports science being allied to the practicalities and difficulties associated with a collision sport. Much of the relevant science has been explained earlier. However, there are certain principles of training which need to be considered:

Overload – the body, or part thereof, will only adapt to a training load, if that load stresses it beyond its present capacity. A training programme must therefore make demands on the body, e.g., heavier weights, running further, etc.

Adaptation – when the body is overloaded, it adapts to cope with the stress.

Progression – as the body adapts it is able to tolerate activity of a greater difficulty. Therefore training loads should be applied in a progressive fashion in order to extend the player's physiological capabilities.

Specificity – training should, as far as possible, be specific to the needs of the game and reflect the demands which players are exposed to during play.

Recovery – the body requires recovery periods, and these should be sufficient both within a session and between training sessions to allow the energy systems to adapt.

Furthermore, it should be noted that, where possible, programmes should be individually based as each player will have an individual genetic make-up, an individual training background, an individual lifestyle, an individual attitude toward training, and individual strengths and weaknesses. This is where objective physiological tests play a big part, along with the coach's own subjective "feel" about the player.

A YEAR LONG CONDITIONING PROGRAMME FOR RUGBY LEAGUE PLAYERS

MONTH	1	2	3	4	5	6	7	8	9	10	11	12
WINTER SEASON	MAY	JUN.	JUL.	AUG.	SEPT.	OCT.	NOV.	DEC.	JAN.	FEB.	MAR.	APRIL
SUMMER SEASON	OCT.	NOV.	DEC.	JAN.	FEB.	MAR.	APRIL	MAY	JUN.	JUL.	AUG.	SEPT.
PERIOD	OFF-SEASON	PRE-SEASON				IN-SEASON						
TESTS	2				3			OPTION				1

FLEXIBILITY: BEFORE AND AFTER EVERY TRAINING SESSION (throughout, months 1–12)

ENDURANCE (Aerobic and Anaerobic):
- Cross training (Month 1)
- Distance runs, fartlek, low intensity runs, jog recovery (aerobic) — Months 2–4
- Distance runs for certain players
- Interval work 400m (anaerobic) → 80m (Months 3–4)
- Interval work – game related plus 80m (anaerobic) → 10m distances dependant upon competition placing (Months 5–12)

STRENGTH:
- Cross training (Month 1)
- MUSCLE GROWTH training for some players (Months 4–5)
- STRENGTH/POWER training for some players
- VARIETY OF GYM WORK FOR MAINTENANCE (in-season)
- Muscular Endurance Circuit → Fast Weights (50%–60% max) → Ultra Slow → Fast Weights (30%–40% max) → Isometrics → Alternative → Body Exercises → Muscular Endurance

SPEED:
- Cross training (Month 1)
- PLYOMETRICS
- SPEED DRILLS
- SPRINTING — Forwards 40m / 80m; Backs 10m / 20m
- Acceleration → Downhill Sprints → Change of Pace → Game related Speed Drills → Acceleration

SKILL:
- Cross training will give general development (Month 1)
- INDIVIDUAL: Basic → Advanced → Advanced and specific
- TEAM: Basic → Advanced → Competition Game Specific

The programmes which follow are intended as guidance and should help every coach feel able to draw up a suitable conditioning programme for his players. However, these programmes are only a beginning and, as the coach gains further confidence and knowledge, it is hoped that he will adapt them for his players' and his team's own needs.

These programmes offer 52-week-a-year advice for players from a zero training age (14–16-year-olds) to more experienced professionals. The diagram on the preceding page shows the adult programme in at-a-glance form but, for details on the programme, it is necessary to study the text which follows.

Training Programme for Adults

OFF-SEASON = Four weeks, with two weeks complete rest and two weeks cross-training.

May (winter season)/October (summer season)

PRE-SEASON = 12 weeks preparation for Rugby League

June–August (winter season)/November–January (summer season)

The Training Week

Monday	Strength training
Tuesday	Anaerobic training
Wednesday	Strength training
Thursday	Speed and power training, including plyometrics
Friday	Strength training
Saturday	Aerobic training
Sunday	Rest

The Programmes

Aerobic training

i) Distance run of 30–40 minutes at moderate intensity, at a steady, even pace; or

ii) Fartlek training; or

iii) Short runs, e.g., 1,000 metres with 30-second jog recovery periods.

The important aspect is to retain the pulse rate at approximately 140 beats per minute.

Anaerobic training

Session 1	=	5 x 400m in 70–74 seconds with 4 minutes' rest
Session 2	=	6 x 400m in 69–73 seconds with 4 minutes' rest
Session 3	=	6 x 300m in 52–55 seconds with 3 minutes' rest
Session 4	=	6 x 300m in 49–52 seconds with 3 minutes' rest
Session 5	=	7 x 200m in 29–31 seconds with 2.5 minutes' rest
Session 6	=	7 x 200m in 29–31 seconds with 2.5 minutes' rest
Session 7	=	7 x 200m in 28–30 seconds with 2.5 minutes' rest
Session 8	=	8 x 200m in 26–28 seconds with 2.5 minutes' rest
Session 9	=	8 x 150m in 21–23 seconds with 2 minutes' rest
Session 10	=	9 x 150m in 20–22 seconds with 1.5 minutes' rest
Session 11	=	10 x 100m in 14–16 seconds with 1 minute's rest
Session 12	=	10 x 80m in 10–12 seconds with 1 minute's rest

Game-related anaerobic training

The duration of effort should be the same as for the pure anaerobic runs above, but the drills should include collisions and resistance training with bags and shields. The coach should include these at every session.

Speed and power training

This session should consist of plyometrics, followed by speed drills, followed by sprinting.

Plyometrics

Weeks 1–4	=	Squat jumps, tuck jumps, double hamstring flicks, ankle hops
Weeks 5–8	=	Slalom, single leg hopping, bounding, side-step
Weeks 9–12	=	Cycled split squats, hop/stride, bunny jump, jump and jump
(Beginners	=	4 sets of 6 repetitions with 30 seconds' rest
One-year experienced and heavy players = 4 x 7 reps with 30 seconds' rest		
One-year experienced and light players = 4 x 8 reps with 30 seconds' rest)		

Speed drills

Weeks 1–4	=	High knees, butt-kickers, skipping
Weeks 5–8	=	Fast arms, toe walk, alternate drive
Weeks 9–12	=	Fast feet plus two other speed drills – coach's choice
Each drill is performed four times over 20 metres with 30 seconds' rest.		

Sprinting

Theme = Top speed, which means that players should build up to the start of the sprint with a jog, i.e., from a rolling start.

	Forwards	Backs	
Weeks 1–3	40m	80m	x 6 reps with 1.5–2 minutes' rest
Weeks 4–6	30m	60m	x 6 reps with 1.5–2 minutes' rest
Weeks 7–9	20m	40m	x 7 reps with 1.5–2 minutes' rest
Weeks 10–12	10m	20m	x 8 reps with 1–1.5 minutes' rest

Strength training

Conducted for three sessions per week for 12 weeks, the programme is dependent on the requirements of the player – either:

a) Strength training for muscle growth

Weeks 1–6	=	Bench press, back squats, upright rows, step-ups, and optional exercises
2 weeks	=	3 sets of 10–12 reps, speed = 402, rest = 60 seconds
2 weeks	=	3 sets of 8–10 reps, speed = 402, rest = 60 seconds
2 weeks	=	3 sets of 12–15 reps, speed = 202, rest = 45 seconds
Weeks 7–12	=	Dips, power cleans (performed quickly), military press, dead lift, and optional exercises
Same sets, reps, speed and rest as in weeks 1–6		

or:

b) Training to develop strength/power

Weeks 1–6	=	Bench press, back squats, upright rows, step-ups
2 weeks	=	3 sets of 3–5 reps, speed = 402, rest = 3 minutes
2 weeks	=	3 sets of 1–3 reps, speed = 4–602, rest = 2.5 minutes
2 weeks	=	3 sets of 5–8 reps, speed = 302, rest = 2 minutes
Weeks 7–12	=	Dips, power cleans, military press, dead lift
Same sets, reps, speed and rest as in weeks 1–6		

Flexibility

Flexibility exercises should always be undertaken, as described in Chapter 7.

IN-SEASON = 36 WEEKS

September – April (winter season)/ February – September (summer season)

The Training Week

The Amateur Player

Monday	Strength training
Tuesday	Conditioning, including anaerobic training and team preparation
Wednesday	Strength training
Thursday	Speed and power training, and team preparation
Friday	Rest
Saturday	Match-day
Sunday	Aerobic training

The Professional Player

Monday	Aerobic training and strength training
Tuesday	Conditioning, including anaerobic training and team preparation
Wednesday	Strength training
Thursday	Speed and power training, and team preparation
Friday	Rest
Saturday	Team preparation
Sunday	Match-day

The Programmes

Aerobic Training

This should take place for one session a week, more if recovering from injury. The day after a match, players should run at a moderate intensity, at a steady, even pace. Fartlek training or short runs with jog recovery are other possibilities. The important aspect is to retain the pulse rate at approximately 140 beats per minute.

Anaerobic training

Sessions 1–4	=	8 x 80m in 10–12 seconds with 60 seconds' rest
Sessions 5–8	=	8 x 60m in 7.5–8.5 seconds with 60 seconds' rest
Sessions 9–12	=	8 x 40m in 5–6 seconds with 40 seconds' rest
Sessions 13–16	=	12 x 20m in 3–3.5 seconds with 20 seconds' rest
Sessions 17–20	=	20 x 10m in 2–2.5 seconds with 15 seconds' rest
Sessions 21–24	=	12 x 20m in 3–4 seconds with 20 seconds' rest
Sessions 25–28	=	10 x 40m in 6–7 seconds with 40 seconds' rest
Sessions 29–32	=	10 x 60m in 7.5–8.5 seconds with 60 seconds' rest
Sessions 33–36	=	10 x 80m in 10–12 seconds with 60 seconds' rest

Game-related drills should also be included here as well, as in the pre-season programme.

Speed and power training

This session should consist of plyometrics, followed by speed drills, followed by sprinting.

Plyometrics

Weeks 1–6	=	as off-season weeks 1–4
Weeks 7–12	=	as off-season weeks 5–8
Weeks 13–18	=	as off-season weeks 9–12

(Heavy and unreceptive players = 4 sets of 8 repetitions with 40 seconds' rest

Light players = 4 sets of 10 repetitions with 45 seconds' rest)

Weeks 19–24	=	Box drills

1. Alternate push-off

2. Stride jump crossover

3. Side-to-side jumps

Each drill is performed with 4 sets of 8 repetitions and 40 seconds' rest

Weeks 25–30	=	Medicine ball drills

1. Chest press

2. Military press throw

3. Trunk rotation

4. Side pass

5. Leg press

Each drill is performed with 3 sets of 8 repetitions and 40 seconds' rest

Weeks 31–36	=	Medicine ball drills

1. Power drop and return

2. Pullover pass

3. Military press throw

4. Hamstring flick

Each drill is performed with 3 sets of 8 repetitions and 40 seconds' rest

Speed drills

These should take place as in the off-season. Each drill should be performed four times over 20–25 metres with 30–40 seconds' rest

Sprinting

Weeks 1–12:	Theme = Acceleration from a standing start.	
	Forwards	Backs
Weeks 1–4	6 x 30m	6 x 60m with full recovery
Weeks 5–8	7 x 20m	7 x 40m with full recovery
Weeks 9–12	8-10 x 10m	8 x 20m with full recovery
Weeks 13–18:	Theme = Downhill sprints, from a jog start	
Weeks 13–15	= 6 x 30m downhill, with full recovery	
Weeks 16–18	= 6 x 30m downhill, then 20m flat, with full recovery	
Weeks 19–24:	Theme = Change of pace, from a jog start	
Weeks 19–21	= 10m sprint, 10m jog, 10m sprint, 10m jog – 6 reps with full recovery	
Weeks 22–24	= 5m sprint, 5m jog, 5m sprint, 5m jog – 7 reps with full recovery	
Weeks 25–33:	Theme = Game-related speed	
The coach should design his own course, 6 reps of 3–6 seconds with full recovery		
Weeks 34–36:	Theme = Acceleration	
	5 x 10m with full recovery	
	10 x 10m with full recovery	
There should be a different start for each sprint, e.g., on the floor, rolling, static, etc.		

Strength training

Weeks 1–4	= Muscular endurance circuit (see Chapter 4)
	Level 1 = 25 reps, 15 seconds' rest, 2 minutes between sets, 3 circuits
	Level 2 = 25 reps, no rest, 2 minutes' rest between sets, 3 circuits
	Level 3 = 30 reps, no rest, 2 minutes' rest between sets, 3 circuits
Weeks 5–10	= Fast weights, with moderate resistance (50–60 per cent of maximum)
	3 x 10 reps at speed 101 with 90 seconds' rest
	3 weeks = Power cleans, jump squats, clap press-ups
	3 weeks = Step-ups, high pull, push press
Weeks 11–16	= Resistance exercises – ultra slow
Weeks 11–13	= Incline bench press, back squat, military press, step-ups
Weeks 14–16	= Bench press. dead lift, upright rows, leg extensions
	3 x 3–5 reps at speed 804 with 2.5 minutes' rest
Weeks 17–22	= Fast weights, with light resistance (30–40 per cent of maximum)
	4 x 15 reps at speed 101 with 90 seconds' rest
	3 weeks = Power cleans, jump squats, clap press-ups
	3 weeks = Step-ups, high pull, push press
Weeks 23–26	= Isometrics
Weeks 23–24	= Eccentric isometric, i.e., with a free weight, the player resists an extreme load (100–120 per cent of maximum) at three points of the descent for 5 seconds in each position. The spotters should assist in returning the weight to the start position. There should be 90 seconds' rest between exercises. Also bench press, back squats, dips, step-ups/downs.
Weeks 25–26	= Concentric isometric, i.e., against a static resistance such as a wall or a weights machine. The player should work at three different positions for 5 seconds each on two upper- and two lower-body exercises.

Weeks 27–29	= Alternative exercises isolating muscle groups, e.g., hamstring curls, shoulder rotation, hip adduction, calf raises, forearm curls, plus one major exercise, 3 x 10 reps at speed 202 with 60–90 seconds' rest
Weeks 30–32	= Body part sessions. 3 x 10 reps at speed 202 with 90 seconds' rest. The coach or the player should choose the routine.
	Legs = squats, hamstring curls, leg extensions, step-ups.
	Chest = bench press, incline bench press, dumb-bell flys, press-ups
	Shoulders = dips, military press, dumb-bell side and front
Weeks 33–36	= Muscular endurance, as in Weeks 1–4

Flexibility

Flexibility exercises should always be undertaken, as described in Chapter 7.

Training Programme for 14–16-year olds

OFF-SEASON = Four weeks, with two weeks complete rest and two weeks cross-training.

May

PRE-SEASON = 12 weeks preparation for Rugby League.

June–August

The Training Week

Monday	Strength training
Tuesday	Anaerobic training
Wednesday	Strength training

Thursday	Anaerobic training
Friday	Speed and power training
Saturday	Aerobic training
Sunday	Rest

The Programmes
Aerobic training

Distance run of 30–40 minutes at a moderate intensity, retaining a pulse rate of between 130–150 beats per minute.

Anaerobic training

Week 1

| Session 1 | = | 4 x 400m in 74–78 seconds with 4 minutes' rest |
| Session 2 | = | 5 x 400m in 74–78 seconds with 4 minutes' rest |

Week 2

| Session 3 | = | 6 x 400m in 72–75 seconds with 4 minutes' rest |
| Session 4 | = | 6 x 400m in 72–75 seconds with 4 minutes' rest |

Week 3

| Session 5 | = | 6 x 300m in 55–58 seconds with 3 minutes' rest |
| Session 6 | = | 6 x 300m in 55–58 seconds with 3 minutes' rest |

Week 4

| Session 7 | = | 6 x 300m in 53–56 seconds with 3 minutes' rest |
| Session 8 | = | 6 x 300m in 53–56 seconds with 3 minutes' rest |

Week 5

| Session 9 | = | 7 x 200m in 32–34 seconds with 2.5 minutes' rest |
| Session 10 | = | 7 x 200m in 32–34 seconds with 2.5 minutes' rest |

Week 6

Session 11	=	7 x 200m in 31–33 seconds with 2.5 minutes' rest
Session 12	=	7 x 200m in 31–33 seconds with 2.5 minutes' rest

Week 7

Session 13	=	7 x 200m in 30–32 seconds with 2.5 minutes' rest
Session 14	=	7 x 200m in 29–31 seconds with 2.5 minutes' rest

Week 8

Session 15	=	8 x 200m in 28–30 seconds with 2.5 minutes' rest
Session 16	=	8 x 200m in 28–30 seconds with 2.5 minutes' rest

Week 9

Session 17	=	8 x 150m in 21–24 seconds with 2 minutes' rest
Session 18	=	8 x 150m in 21–24 seconds with 2 minutes' rest

Week 10

Session 19	=	9 x 150m in 20–23 seconds with 2 minutes' rest
Session 20	=	9 x 150m in 20–23 seconds with 2 minutes' rest

Week 11

Session 21	=	10 x 100m in 15–18 seconds with 1.5 minutes' rest
Session 22	=	10 x 100m in 15–18 seconds with 1.5 minutes' rest

Week 12

Session 23	=	10 x 80m in 12–14 seconds with 1 minute's rest
Session 24	=	10 x 80m in 12–14 seconds with 1 minute's rest

Speed and power training

This session should consist of plyometrics, followed by speed drills, followed by sprinting.

Plyometrics

Weeks 1–6	=	Squat jumps, tuck jumps, ankle hops
Weeks 7–12	=	Side-step, slalom

Five reps of each drill are performed as quickly as possible in four sets, with 30 seconds' rest in between.

Speed drills

Weeks 1–6	=	High knees, butt-kickers
Weeks 7–12	=	Fast feet, skipping

Each drill is performed 3 times over 15m with 30 seconds' rest

Sprinting

Theme = Top speed, which means that players should build up to the start of the sprint with a jog, i.e., from a rolling start.

	Forwards	Backs	
Weeks 1–3	50m	70m	x 6 reps with full recovery
Weeks 4–6	40m	50m	x 7 reps with full recovery
Weeks 7–9	30m	35m	x 8 reps with full recovery
Weeks 10–12	15m	20m	x 9 reps with full recovery

Strength training

> **Weeks 1–4**: Summer routine A
>
> Bench press, leg curls, seated row, back squats (90°), trunk curls
>
> **Weeks 5–8**: Summer routine B
>
> Incline bench press, leg extensions, lat pull-downs, step-ups, chinnie sit-ups
>
> **Weeks 9–12**: Summer routine C
>
> Dips, calf raises, upright rows, dead lift, reverse abdominal curl
>
> **Year 1** = 3 sets of 15 repetitions at 2 seconds per rep, with 90 seconds' rest
>
> **Year 2** = 3 sets of 10 repetitions at 4 seconds per rep, with 90 seconds' rest

Flexibility

Flexibility exercises should be undertaken both before every training session, holding the stretch for 8–10 seconds and repeating each stretch twice; and, after every training session, holding the stretch for 30–60 seconds just once.

IN-SEASON = 36 weeks

September–April

The Training Week

Monday	–	Aerobic training
Tuesday	–	Strength training
Wednesday	–	Anaerobic training incorporated in club training
Thursday	–	Strength training
Friday	–	Speed/power incorporated in club training
Saturday	–	Rest
Sunday	–	Match-day

The Programmes
Aerobic training

Distance run for 20–30 minutes at a low to medium intensity, retaining a pulse rate of 120–140 beats per minute.

Anaerobic training

Sessions 1–4	=	8 x 80m in 11–13 seconds with 60 seconds' rest
Sessions 5–8	=	8 x 60m in 8–9.5 seconds with 60 seconds' rest
Sessions 9–12	=	8 x 40m in 6.5–7 seconds with 40 seconds' rest
Sessions 13–16	=	12 x 20m in 3–3.5 seconds with 20 seconds' rest
Sessions 17–20	=	20 x 10m in 2–2.5 seconds with 15 seconds' rest
Sessions 21–24	=	12 x 20m in 3–3.5 seconds with 20 seconds' rest
Sessions 25–28	=	10 x 40m in 6.5–7 seconds with 40 seconds' rest
Sessions 29–32	=	10 x 60m in 8–9.5 seconds with 60 seconds' rest
Sessions 33–36	=	10 x 80m in 11–13 seconds with 60 seconds' rest

Speed and power training

Plyometrics

Weeks 1-8	=	Side cone jumps, diagonal cone jumps, forward cone jumps
Weeks 9-16	=	Hamstring flicks, bunny jumps, jump and jump
Weeks 17-24	=	Squat jumps, tuck jumps, ankle hops
Weeks 25-32	=	Slalom, side-step
Weeks 33-36	=	No plyometrics

7 reps of each drill are performed as fast as possible in 4 sets with 30 seconds' rest in between.

Speed drills

Weeks 1–6	=	High knees, butt-kickers
Weeks 7–12	=	Fast feet, skipping
Weeks 13–18	=	Fast feet, toe walk

Each drill is performed 3 times over 15m.

Weeks 19–24	=	As weeks 1–6
Weeks 25–30	=	As weeks 7–12
Weeks 31–36	=	As weeks 13–18

Each drill is performed 3 times over 20m with 30 seconds' rest.

Sprinting

Weeks 1–12: Theme = Acceleration, from a standing start

	Forwards	Backs
Weeks 1–4	6 x 30m	6 x 60m with full recovery
Weeks 5–8	7 x 20m	7 x 40m with full recovery
Weeks 9–12	8-10 x 10m	8 x 20m with full recovery

Weeks 13–18: Theme = Downhill sprints, from a jog start

Weeks 13–15	6 x 30m downhill, with full recovery
Weeks 16–18	6 x 30m downhill, then 20m flat, with full recovery

Weeks 19–24: Theme = Change of pace, from a jog start

Weeks 19–21	10m sprint, 10m jog, 10m sprint, 10m jog – 6 reps with full recovery
Weeks 22–24	5m sprint, 5m jog, 5m sprint, 5m jog – 7 reps with full recovery

Weeks 25–32: Theme = Game-related speed

The coach should design his own course, 6 reps of 3–6 seconds with full recovery

Weeks 33–36: Theme = Acceleration

6 x 10m with full recovery

10 x 5m with full recovery

These should be a different start for each sprint, e.g., on the floor, rolling, static, etc.

Strength training

To be conducted for two sessions a week.

Weeks 1–4   =   Muscular endurance circuit

20 reps of each exercise (see Chapter 4), 20 seconds' rest between exercises with 2 minutes' rest between sets, 3 circuits

Weeks 5–8   =   Summer routine A

Weeks 9–12   =   Summer routine B

Weeks 13–16   =   Summer routine C

Weeks 17–22   =   Arm curls, leg extensions, dumb-bell flys, calf raises

Weeks 23–28   =   Tricep extensions, leg press, dumb-bell side raises, lunges

Weeks 29–32   =   Neck resistance (three-way) forearm curls, sprint curls

Year 1   =   3 sets of 15 repetitions at 2 seconds per rep, with 90 seconds' rest

Year 2   =   3 sets of 10 repetitions at 4 seconds per rep, with 90 seconds' rest

Weeks 33–36   =   Muscular endurance circuit

20 reps of each exercise (see Chapter 4), 15 seconds' rest between exercises with 2 minutes' rest between sets, 3 circuits

Flexibility

Flexibility exercises should be undertaken as in the off- and pre-season schedules.

Bibliography

1. *Strength and Power in Sport* (1992)

    Koni P, Blackwell Scientific, London

2. *Essentials of Strength Training and Conditioning* (1994)

    Baechle T, Human Kinetics, Illinois USA

3. *Matrix for Muscle Gain* (1993)

    Laura R, Allen and Unwin, NSW Australia

4. *The Olympic Book of Sports Medicine* (1988)

    Blackwell Scientific, London

5. *The Physiology of Sport and Exercise* (1994)

    Costill D, Wilmore J, Human Kinetics, Illinois USA

6. *Science and Practice of Strength Training* (1995)

    Zatsiorsky V, Human Kinetics, Illinois USA

7. *Exercise Physiology* (1988)

    Mcardle W, Katch V, Katch F, Lea and Febiger, Philadelphia USA

8. *Designing Resistance Training Programmes* (1988)

    Fleck S, Kraemer W, Human Kinetics, Illinois USA

9. *Quantum Strength and Power Training* (1995)

O'Shea P, Patricks Books, Corvalis USA

10. *Physiology of Fitness* (1990)

Sharkey B, Human Kinetics, Illinois USA

11. *Sports Training Principles* (1989)

Dick F, A & C Black, London

12. *Strength Training for Rugby* (1990)

Walsh B, Kangaroo Press, Sydney

13. *Speed Strength Training for Football* (1992)

Kreiss E, Taylor Sports Publishing, USA

14. *Sport Speed* (1988)

Dintiman G, Ward R, Leisure Press, Illinois USA

15. *Strength Training for Football* (1993)

Pauletto B, Human Kinetics, Illinois USA

16. *Strength Training and Conditioning for Speed Development* (1988)

NSCA, Nebraska USA

17. *Plyometrics – A Legitimate Form of Training* (1988)

Duda M, Physician and Sports Medicine Vol 16, No. 3

18. *A Review of Plyometric Training* (1991)

     Lundin P, Berg W, NSCA Journal, Vol 6, No. 3

19. *Developing Explosive Muscular Power* (1994)

     Newton R, Kraemer W, NSCA Journal, Oct 1994

20. *Plyometric Training* (1993)

     King I, Sport (Coaching Association of Canada) Vol 13, No. 5

21. *Sprint Training* (1990)

     Ozolin E, Soviet Sports Review, December

22. *Muscles and the Sprint* (1992)

     Atletika L, Fitness and Sports Review International

23. *Dictionary of Sport and Exercise Science* (1991)

     Anshell et al., Human Kinetics, Illinois USA

24. *Jumping into Plyometrics* (1992)

     Chu D, Leisure Press

25. *Strength Training for Young Athletes* (1993)

     Kraemer W, Fleck S, Human Kinetics, Illinois USA

26. *Plyometrics – Explosive Power Training* (1985)

     Radcliffe J and Farentinos R, Human Kinetics, Illinois USA

27. *A Study of the Major Reasons behind the Strength of Australian Rugby League* (1985)

Phil Larder

28. *The Psychological Preparation of Football Players*

Davey (taken from *The World Congress of Science and Football* Ed. T Reilly,

London (1988))

29. *American Visit Report* (1985)

Phil Larder

30. *The Rugby League Coaching Manual* (1988)

Larder P, Heinemann Kingswood

31. *Body Fat Assessed from Total Body Density and its Estimation from Skinfold Thickness* (1974)

Durwin J and Wormersley J, from *British Journal of Nutrition*, Vol 32 pp77–92

32. *Theory and Methodology of Training*

Bompa, Kendall Hunt Publishing Company, Iowa (1983)

Acknowledgements

The authors would like to thank all the people who have made this publication possible. We should particularly like to thank Maurice P. Lindsay and the Board of Directors at the Rugby Football League who commissioned the original study by Andy Clarke which was the starting point of this text. Neil Tunnicliffe, Project Co-ordinator at the Rugby Football League also deserves a special mention for his expertise and time editing the book.

It would be remiss of us not to acknowledge the great influence of Rod Mackenzie and Phil Larder on the subject of Physical Conditioning for Rugby League which started the fitness revolution in the game.

Our thanks go also to John Brewer and all at the Lilleshall Human Performance Centre, Sue Bowden, Coaching Secretary and all the players, Marvin Golden, Iestyn Harris, Francis Cummins, Paul Rowley, Simon Haughton and Kris Radlinski for their photogenic qualities.

All the photographs in this book are published by kind permission of Varley-Wilkinson Picture Agency.